Arthur,
You have bee
friend for a lifeti
you have been my hear

Victor

Dr. Good Has Gone
Recollections of a Greenwich Village Physician

VICTOR KEYLOUN, M.D.

To my soul mate,
It has been one wild, wonderful ride.

ACKNOWLEDGMENT:

To Michael: my son, my editor, and the man who has pestered me to make this story better than I could have done on my own.

Carol

Doctors' wives get a bum rap. When a doctor's wife raises a health-related complaint to her husband, she is often dismissed like a third year medical student who imagines she has every disease she's ever read about in the textbooks of medicine. Every headache is a brain tumor, every bellyache is an ulcer, and every hemorrhoid is cancer. The wife of a doctor learns not to complain to her husband. Instead, she seeks counsel from someone else, and often from someone affiliated with another institution, lest her husband learn of her inquiry through a thriving gossip mill. She might also withhold the fact that her husband is a doctor until she's certain she's received an objective assessment.

Every marriage of any duration experiences rough patches. Mine was no exception. I had been married to my wife Carol for twenty-three years when the silly and petty quibbles common to a relationship began to become serious arguments. They centered on the usual culprits: working too late, inattention, boredom, and our differences raising our son. One morning, I came downstairs to have breakfast after a long night of bickering, and tried to make one last point to bolster the position I had taken the night before. Carol turned to me and said, "I have Parkinson's disease." My knees buckled. I was stunned. She collapsed in my arms in a flood of tears. All I could do was hug her. There were no words of solace. All thoughts relative to our disagreements disappeared into the ether.

After a long while I asked, "How do you know?"

"I went to see a neurologist."

"Who?" I asked.

"No one you know. He was recommended by a friend." She wiped her face with her hands and went into the kitchen to wash some dishes. "You should get going," she said over her shoulder. "You'll be late."

There was still so much I wanted to know, but I could see that she didn't want to talk any more about it. I might have pried the full story from her, but since Carol was otherwise in good health, I reasoned it wasn't an urgent matter. A discussion could wait until dinner time, so I let her have her space, and I left for work.

All day, my thoughts drifted. Why didn't she confide in me about her symptoms? Why didn't she ask me to refer a neurologist? Was she just asserting independence? Or did she think I would dismiss her complaints? Was this the real reason behind our disagreements? I tried to focus, but my thoughts centered on what would lie ahead. In my practice, I had treated many patients with Parkinson's disease, so I knew where Carol's journey would lead, and I knew what my role would be in it.

When I returned home that night, Carol had my cocktail waiting for me as always. She put dinner on the table as if the morning outburst had never happened, and we talked about everything and anything, except the obvious elephant in the room. She related stories about the miserable cards she was dealt at bridge. I complained about traffic on the Long Island Expressway. The conversation was ritualistic, bland and inoffensive.

Once we had finished eating, I asked Carol what had prompted her to seek the advice of a neurologist.

"I've had this twitch," she said, looking absently at her left hand, "between my ring finger and my pinky. I thought it was a pinched nerve or something in my neck." Carol had often complained of pain in her neck and back for all the years we were married. "I thought it would go away, but it's been months. So I went to see someone." All of a sudden, her fury erupted. "But I've never met such a cold-hearted son of a bitch! He was the most unfeeling, uncaring man I have ever met."

Apparently, while taking her history, the neurologist was distant to the point of being emotionless. Carol sat in his office, nervously waiting to hear what he had discovered. He sat before her, smug and quite proud of himself, and announced with total indifference, "You have Parkinson's disease."

"Are you sure?" she asked, incredulous.

With a smirk on his face, the neurologist said, "Surely, you must have known!"

Carol was more infuriated with his attitude and lack of compassion than the diagnosis itself. I noticed, during the entirety of her story, she never once referred to him as "doctor." When she finished, the rage with which she cursed the neurologist turned immediately to abject woe, and she began to weep.

"What scares me most, Vic," she choked through tears, "is ending up in some nursing home."

"Carol," I reassured her, "so long as I am alive, that will never happen."

In my mind's eye I watched every dream I ever had about our future shatter. All the things I looked forward to doing in retirement, every trip I imagined taking to far away places, they all evaporated. I looked at my wife and imagined, too, the dreams she might have had for the future, and the reality that lay before her. But for whatever reason, the thought that echoed loudest in my mind at that moment was the aphorism "He who treats himself has a fool for a physician." By extension, it also applies to caring for family members. You can be a physician, you can be a husband, but you can't be both.

I could, however, do everything possible and use every resource I had to ensure that Carol received the best treatment available. The first thing I needed to do was to confirm her diagnosis. I made an appointment with William Doherty, a neurologist I frequently used to call in consultation. Carol knew him from the hospital, and that helped to establish a bond. He was mature, seasoned, calm, and warm. Carol presented her chief complaint and history while I purposely sat aside and listened. I heard the entire story for the first time in chronological order.

After a thorough neurologic exam, William sat down with both of us to discuss his findings. Much to his credit, he spoke to my wife as if I were not present. Sitting there, watching and listening to William and Carol, I marveled at his ability to speak with her in a way that was caring, friendly, and reassuring in the face of such impending hardship. I wondered who that first neurologist was, and where he had been trained. Not that it mattered. I have seen first hand a shift in medicine since I started my career. It is a far cry from the cottage industry I joined back in the 1960s.

Medical School

It was 1956 when I entered medical school. Georgetown University was undergoing a rebirth. It had always been a good school, but the Jesuit administration had embarked on a campaign to make it great. Part of that process was to recruit teachers who could elevate the level of pedagogy. No longer a catch-all of part-time instructors, basic sciences were now taught by a dedicated, full-time staff of academic physicians.

Harvard and Yale produced academics. Georgetown produced clinicians.

One of the professors Georgetown recruited was Dr. Harold Jaegers, a renowned educator who held the title of Professor of Medicine. Dr. Jaegers left a lasting legacy at the University, having developed an exhaustive protocol for asking questions. Every conceivable question one could ask of a patient was published in a little pamphlet and distributed to every student. When we began to interface with patients, we were taught to first determine the chief complaint. One might ask, "Why did you come to see me?" or "What seems to be the trouble?" It may appear simple, but in many cases, it required a little probing. Sometimes patients cannot focus on why they go to see a doctor. Their problem might be vague: "I don't feel well." There could also be multiple complaints: "I have pain when I eat, my back hurts, and I can't get to sleep at night." It was imperative to get to the real reason for the visit. Once we sorted through and identified the true chief complaint, we needed to determine the history of the present illness. This required us to focus on the organ system of the chief complaint and ask all relevant questions to get a sense of when the problem began, how intense were its symptoms, its distribution, and whether it radiated to other parts of the body.

The essence of the Jaegers methodology came into full focus in a section called the review of systems. If, for example, a patient presented with a headache, and after asking all the relevant probing questions, it was obvious that the person had a sinus infection, we were still required to ask all the questions relating to each and every other organ system. Every question relative to the cardiac, pulmonary, gastrointestinal, genitourinary, musculoskeletal, and neurologic systems was asked of every patient. The tedious part of such a thorough review was writing the answer to each question in long hand. If done correctly, a twenty-page report was submitted to the professor. We did this on each and every patient we encountered in medical school, and were only allowed to abbreviate the writing in our final year. But it was still expected that we asked all the questions. By then, they had become part of our psyche.

The first two years of medical school were spent primarily in the classroom and the laboratories. We dissected a cadaver, studied tissue under a microscope and performed biochemical tests that today would seem quaint. We performed surgery on dogs, studied their physiology and interpolated the findings to human anatomy and physiology.

One of the boldest innovations that Georgetown University embarked upon was to integrate psychiatry into the curriculum. For decades, psychiatry had been considered part of the neurology discipline. As more was understood about psychiatric disorders, it became clear that they were not, in fact, disorders of the nervous system, and psychiatry was split off as a separate and distinct discipline. Georgetown was among the first medical schools to introduce students to the specialty as part of its curriculum. We had formal didactic lectures that dealt with depression, psychoses, phobias, and personality disorders.

I recall one lecture, however, that stands as a testament to how early in its infancy the specialty was, and specifically how muddled the perception and understanding of homosexuality was. The professor began with the statement that homosexuality was a psychiatric disorder. Vestiges of Freudian psychology were incorporated in the lecture, but for the most part, it consisted of prejudicial and anecdotal examples. To be sure, the professor appeared most uncomfortable during his dissertation, frequently mopping rivulets of sweat from his brow with a handkerchief while haltingly attempting to articulate the right words and phrases to describe a homosexual relationship between two men. He made a valiant effort to explain the psychodynamics of this "illness" and its genesis, attributing it to being raised to adulthood under the thumb of an overbearing, domineering mother and an ineffectual father.

Despite the fact that, up until that time, I had never known anyone who was overtly or admittedly homosexual, the explanation sounded as far-fetched to me then as it sounds to me today. It didn't encompass lesbians. It didn't encompass gay people raised by single parents. It simply didn't ring true, and for the first time in my academic career, I questioned the authority and competence of a teacher.

The second two years of medical school were spent almost exclusively in various hospitals throughout the District of Columbia and northern Virginia, serving as "acting interns" under the tutelage of senior residents. We performed intake interviews and physical examinations on newly admitted patients. The clerkships ran for weeks at a time and afforded us the opportunity to see and observe the treatment of a cornucopia of pathology. As part of the new curriculum, this included clerkships in psychiatric wards.

Three patients are indelible in my memory. One fellow I recall presented to the clinic with a complaint of impotence. He was in his mid-thirties and worked for the government. He had a highly sensitive job, had access to information of a top-secret, classified nature, and was required to keep that information in the strictest of confidence. The pressure of maintaining such secrecy ultimately manifested itself in his inability to initiate an erection. We called it "transference" then. Once he was able to make the connection between his job-related stress and its psychosomatic response, he went on to engage in a healthy sexual relationship with a woman.

That encounter was most instructive for me. The relationship between mind and body could not have been made clearer.

Another case centered on a woman who refused to leave her place of employment. She also worked for the government. No amount of persuasion could motivate her to leave the building. The police were called and she was summarily brought to the D.C. General Hospital's psychiatric ward. I was assigned to do the intake interview and physical examination. The patient was twenty-two years old. She had flaming red hair and freckles galore. She was exceptionally beautiful and could easily have been a model. She sat adjacent to my desk, accompanied by a matron (as was the custom). As I began to ask her questions, she removed her johnny coat. She was now stark naked. The matron quickly replaced the hospital gown. Within seconds, the patient removed it. We went through this dance for almost a half hour. It wasn't clear to me if she was attempting to be seductive or if she had some other motivation (she was so totally devoid of emotion), but it seemed she could not communicate with me unless she was naked. I was all of twenty-four years old. To say the experience was awkward would be the understatement of all time. We struggled through the interview and the physical exam. I never understood her need to be naked, and I never had anyone explain to my satisfaction what the dynamic was of that behavior. My clerkship ended and I never learned what became of her. My lasting impression was that her behavior was pitiable.

During that same clerkship, I was told to do an intake interview and examine a woman who had been admitted the previous night. She was in her room and refused to be transported to the doctor's office. As I entered her room, I found a woman sobbing hysterically. She was lying in bed, facing the wall, her body curled in the fetal position. I noticed that she was clutching something in her hand but could not immediately determine what the object was. She mentioned to me that her husband had died but offered no other information. I did everything I could to console her but to no avail. Finally, I asked her what she was holding in her hand and she said it was a picture of her husband. I asked to see it, and after a long consideration, she slowly loosened her grip on the photo so that I could remove it from her hand.

It was a picture of Jesus Christ!

When I presented my history and results of the physical exam to the attending psychiatrist, he confirmed my diagnosis of schizophrenia. The only remedy at the time was electroshock therapy and rest in a long-term psychiatric facility. I did not have the opportunity to follow her clinical course and I always wondered what became of her.

These experiences motivated me to consider psychiatry as a career. The dynamics were fascinating. Unfortunately, specific therapy was largely absent, and after much thought, I elected to pursue my initial interest in internal medicine. But this exposure to psychiatry—while not comprehensive—still permeated my practice of medicine. It helped considerably to make me a better doctor.

As students we were exposed to so much. We performed spinal taps, drew fluid from the abdomen of patients with ascites, inserted chest tubes and sutured lacerations in emergency rooms. We inserted Foley catheters and Levine tubes on a regular basis. We prescribed medication to hospitalized patients. While superiors always reviewed our actions, review rarely occurred before our decisions took full effect.

Ours was a baptism by fire. Nowhere in this country is a medical student allowed to assume this kind of responsibility anymore. Patients' rights groups have lobbied against allowing unlicensed medical students to perform the procedures we carried out routinely. Laws prevent abuse of work rules. So far as I know, no one suffered at the hands of any of my fellow classmates. Perhaps we were lucky. There is no doubt, however, that we were well equipped to begin internship and assume responsibility head-on.

Upon graduation from medical school, I interviewed with Dr. Harold Winters, Chief of Medicine at St. Vincent's Hospital in Greenwich Village, New York City. I was awarded an internship at the hospital. I elected to do my mandatory military service after internship, before I began my three years of residency training. Dr. Winters had a residency position waiting for me upon my return from service in the U.S. Navy.

When I had completed my residency, I was offered a full time salaried appointment at the hospital. In hindsight, that offer was a harbinger of a drastic change in medicine. A new government program called "Medicare" was about to come into play, and a consultant who claimed an inside track to the new insurance policy convinced the nuns who ran the hospital that, by putting doctors on salary, the hospital stood to make more money by billing Medicare in their doctors' stead. The doctors would no longer receive a fee for service, but instead would have the "stability" of a guaranteed salary, and the hospital would be free to pocket the surplus.

I opted to decline the offer. After all the years of study, training and military service, I didn't want to be just an employee. Everyone in my family was self-employed, and I shared their entrepreneurial nature, even if I had ventured away from the family business. However, in order to maintain a civil relationship with the hospital, I negotiated for half-time employment. In return for a smaller stipend, I would be expected to supervise residents for half of the year and read all of the electrocardiograms the hospital generated during the year. It wasn't quite a fair deal, but it left me free to strike out on my own.

My First

My private practice began on Friday, July 1, 1966. I was thirty-one years old, married for less than two months, and had moved with my bride into an apartment only the day before. Having just returned from our honeymoon, my wife and I spent the first few days in our new home unpacking our wedding presents and storing things in cupboards and closets. My mind really wasn't into it. I had been chief resident for a year, overseeing the ward service and clinics in one of the busiest hospitals in New York, and now I had absolutely nothing to do. Looming were the expenses of office rent, a telephone, an answering service, malpractice insurance, and a new contraption called a "beeper," which the answering service employed to alert me that someone had called. It was daunting.

I could not afford to rent an entire office for myself, so I had arranged to sublet space several afternoons a week from Dr. Hannibal De Bellis, an elderly doctor with a shrinking practice. Dr. De Bellis was one of the founding members of the American College of Cardiology and of the Salmagundi Club. A noted sculptor, Hannibal had been commissioned by the United States Navy to produce medals of heroic admirals and statues depicting noted battles. He used the back room of the office to create the clay models of his subjects.

When I signed the lease, Dr. De Bellis gave me a piece of advice: if I had only three patients to see in an afternoon, I should schedule them all at the same time. I asked him why.

"Patients like to see a busy doctor," he said, "If there's no one in the waiting room, they'll question your competence!"

The advice was particularly amusing, considering I hadn't a single patient in my care, never mind three, but the De Bellis Rule stood the test of time.

My professional responsibilities were a cipher. I checked my beeper almost hourly. I called my answering service almost as often, only to be told that no one had called. I had spent all my savings from my Navy pay on Carol's engagement ring and on our honeymoon. Carol worked in the chemistry lab at St. Vincent's, but the thought of living on her salary rankled me, even if it were only for a few months. Luckily, I had secured several part-time assignments as a physician for a number of businesses and institutions across town, but it being a holiday weekend, I couldn't go to any of them.

I paced about, uncertain of my future. My restlessness exasperated Carol. In the middle of stacking dishes in the cupboard, she turned to me and implored, "Will you stop?!" I thought for a moment she was going to throw one of the dishes at me. "You've been in practice for two whole days," she said. "What did you expect?"

Carol was a take charge lady who suffered no fool, least of all her new husband.

St. Vincent's Hospital was a nine-hundred-bed, voluntary hospital chartered and managed by the Sisters of Charity. Opened in 1849, it was the first Catholic hospital in New York City, and began as a small limestone building in the East Village. It was later relocated to the corner of Seventh Avenue and Eleventh Street, and over the ensuing century, six more buildings were added: a clinic, two structures for private patients, a psychiatric pavilion, a nursing school and a chapel large enough to be a church in its own right. In its entirety, the hospital wrapped around Seventh Avenue halfway up Eleventh and Twelfth Streets.

The Elizabeth Baley Seton Building was the primary hospital building, and was home to the wards, where the indigent and uninsured were treated, and where I had done most of my training. It was a majestic, seven-story Georgian edifice, featuring oversized windows that welcomed a steady stream of sunshine from the south and east. The corridors were laid with beautifully patterned tile and polished to a sheen on a daily basis. Every floor had two dedicated nurses' stations, one at either end of the central corridor, to which pneumatic tubes delivered medicine and supplies.

The wards were compartmentalized by floor into units dedicated to surgery, medicine, and obstetrics, and further subdivided by area into male and female wards. Some wards had as few as four beds, and others had as many as fourteen. During times of high occupancy (especially winter, when fractures and pneumonia were rampant), temporary beds were even deployed in the corridors.

The buildings dedicated to private (paying) patients were equally pristine, if somewhat less majestic. Rooms in these buildings provided for much more privacy, each designed to house two patients. On the tenth floor were single rooms for those individuals willing to pay extra. In some cases, patients with infectious diseases requiring isolation were placed in these single rooms.

It was a sprawling complex, home to some of the most extraordinarily talented nurses in the world, and a magnet for young physicians who wanted a taste of medicine in a big city, in a hospital with superior teaching. It provided care to those from all walks of life: from giants in industry to retired little old ladies to downtrodden alcoholics. Servicing the neighborhoods of Greenwich Village, Chelsea and NoHo, St. Vincent's also boasted one of the busiest emergency rooms in the city.

One of the principal sources of referral for a doctor starting practice was the emergency room. Any patient who entered the emergency room who was not under the care of an attending physician would have been admitted to the ward service, where a resident physician and his intern would care for him under the supervision of an attending physician. That is, unless the patient requested the service of a private doctor. In that case, it was customary for the admitting office to offer the names of three physicians for consideration. Among those names would be the doctors who had recently completed their residency training.

On July 3, 1966, a gentleman entered the emergency room with a heart attack. He wanted a private doctor. Of the three physicians names offered to him, he chose mine.

Calling from the admitting office at St. Vincent's, the disembodied voice on the phone was music to my ears.

"May I tell the man that you are willing to accept him as a private patient, Dr. Keyloun?"

"HELL YES, I'LL ACCEPT HIM!" I wanted to shout. What I actually said was, "Certainly. Please tell the patient that I will be over to see him as soon as possible."

Thinking back on it, my response might even have been accompanied by a dramatic sigh.

Six years had elapsed from the first day of my internship to the start of private practice. Over the course of those years, I had attended many patients. During internship and residency training, there was always someone senior who could be called upon for advice. (Realistically, someone was always looking over my shoulder.) During my two years in the Navy,

I was the lone physician on a destroyer tender, and also took sick call at the Mayport Naval Air Station in Florida. During my second year of military service, I was assigned to the Mare Island Naval Shipyard in Vallejo, California. There were five other physicians from whom I could seek counsel and advice. Still, there was so much time on my hands that I engaged in a little moonlighting. A local physician became ill, so I took over his practice while he recovered.

All this is to say I was accustomed to accepting responsibility for the care of others. But nothing had prepared me for the feeling I experienced when that clerk in the admitting office told me a patient had selected me to be his doctor. As excited as I was to have my first private patient, I realized in the seconds it took me to respond to the clerk that, in private practice, there is no back up. You are "it."

That first patient's name was Solomon Rothstein. He lived on the Lower East Side of Manhattan, which had been an enclave for Jewish immigrants for over a century. I took his history and examined him. I reviewed his electrocardiogram and chest X-ray. Since he was my very first patient and I had no other, I saw him at least three times (if not four times) each day of his hospitalization. He made an uneventful recovery, and I discharged him from the hospital with advice to see me two weeks later in my office.

His arrival for his post-hospitalization visit was punctual. He was most cordial and grateful. He believed that I had saved his life, when nothing was further from the truth. At last, he asked, "So, what kind of a name is Keyloun?"

"Well, both my parents came here as teenagers from Syria in the early 1900s," I replied.

"Oy! *Mein Gott*," he cried, eyes wide with panic. "You're an Arab! You're gonna kill me."

"Solomon! Calm down," I pleaded. I wasn't sure if he was teasing me or testing me. "If I didn't kill you in the hospital, why would I kill you now?"

Solomon looked at me for what seemed like an eternity. Slowly, his lips formed something close to a half-smile. Squinting in concentration, he stared at me for several seconds before making a pronouncement.

"You're a good doctor. I like you."

The walk home from my office was like dancing on a cloud. I couldn't wait to tell Carol about my day. As we sat down for dinner, I shared the conversation I had with Sol. It made her smile.

"You know, when I first told my parents about you, they were concerned." Carol's parents had emigrated from Italy as young adults, and had never met anyone from Syria. "They didn't know what to expect!"

"They must have thought I'd show up wearing a *keffiyeh* and a *disdasha*!" I joked.

"Well, when you came over that first time in that business suit, I have to admit," Carol said, ladling some pasta in my plate, "you looked like a real nerd."

"I'm glad I didn't disappoint them."

Her face lit up, and with a hint of a tease in her voice, she replied, "My father was so happy to get me out of the house, I could have brought home a felon and he would have been happy."

"Like I said, I'm glad I didn't disappoint."

Alcohol and Addiction

The office I shared with Dr. De Bellis was located at the foot of Fifth Avenue, just two blocks north of the majestic arch that frames the entrance to Washington Square Park. I could not afford (nor did I have need for) a full-time secretary, so I posted a note offering part-time employment in the student lounge at nearby New York University. Because my office hours were in the late afternoon after most classes had finished, there was ample interest. I hired a young woman named Robin, whose above-average grades reassured me that she could work a few hours every week with me without interfering with her studies. She answered the phone, sat in when I examined female patients, and handled the billing. Naturally, she quit once she graduated, and left a huge void in my daily routine.

At about the same time that I lost Robin, our landlord sent us a letter informing us that he was about to triple our rent. Dr. De Bellis and I thought it was a typographical error. The landlord refused to negotiate with us. His "take it or leave it" attitude was the final straw that forced Dr. De Bellis to retire. I was left to find an affordable office of my own. I was fortunate to find one on Twelfth Street, across the street from the New School for Social Research.

As fate would have it, a young woman came to see me late one afternoon. She complained of a vaginal discharge and severe abdominal pain. It required that I do a pelvic examination and an analysis of the discharge, but not having yet replaced Robin, I had no one to assist me. I told her it was inappropriate for me to examine her without a witness present. She cringed, and begged me to reconsider. She couldn't wait another day. Against my better judgment, I went ahead with the examination, and found her to be suffering from a classic case of candidiasis, a yeast infection of the vagina. I prescribed an antifungal agent, and upon her return a week later, her examination was normal.

As she was paying me for the office visit, she asked, "Don't you have a secretary to handle this?"

"Not at the moment, no," I said.

"Why not?"

"Well, no one has stepped forward to accept the job!"

"I'll take it!"

It was the beginning of an extraordinary relationship.

Maureen hailed from Woodside, an amorphous district in the borough of Queens. Her mother was Irish and her father was Spanish. Maureen inherited the best of both gene pools. She was on the far side of pretty. She had blonde hair, blue eyes, and a sea of freckles. Once settled at her desk in the waiting room, she was a tornado of activity, organizing charts, ordering my lunch, collecting messages from the answering service, and answering the phone. She never left before I did—often late at night.

Even though she was only in her early twenties, Maureen's best quality was her uncanny ability to relate to people. She was charming and gracious. More than anything else, she was empathetic. She treated my patients with dignity and respect, and was always available to talk with them and put them at ease. She was affable and funny. I once heard a patient tell her that she didn't have the money with her to pay for my fee. Without skipping a beat, Maureen quipped, "Well, I'll just have to lock you in the closet until you find it," whereupon both laughed uproariously.

In those first years, my practice grew at a snail's pace. As a doctor new to solo practice, I looked after patients with obsessive zeal and diligence. If they were hospitalized, I'd visit them three or four times per day, having nothing else to do with my time. Eventually, they would recover and go home to resume their normal lives. I might not see them again for months. Often were the times I would lie awake at night, wondering why my patients hadn't returned, wondering whether they thought my care was good enough. But then, when a thirty-two-year-old man whom I had treated for pneumonia appeared in my office after a two-year absence, it dawned on me that the hiatus existed because the patient had been healthy!

It took me almost three years to earn enough money in the office to cover the expenses of the office. I had to supplement my income with part-time jobs in industry, performing executive examinations at such places as Western Electric, Time & Life Publishing, the International Longshoreman's Association Union, Goodbody & Co., and AT&T. These jobs were handed down like heirlooms from one newly-minted practicing physician to another. It was reassuring to see the name of a Chief of Service in the record book of one of those corporations. The signatures of physicians familiar to me confirmed the fact that we all begin humbly.

As a young doctor trying to develop a practice with a steady stream of patients to fill office hours and maintain a census at the hospital, I was struck by how selective many physicians who practiced at St. Vincent's were about accepting new patients. They chose to allow only those who could afford their fees, those whose lifestyle was compatible with theirs, and those whom they deemed "suitable." The ones they did not like were given excuses.

"My practice is full."

"I'm sorry, I just don't know enough about your illness. You should find another doctor."

"You'd be better served in a clinic."

I questioned the wisdom of my peers and mentors who rated prospective patients. It had the earmarks of prejudice.

Those whom others perceived to be marginal patients, I welcomed openly. No one was refused. They were like my next-door neighbors. Many were as poor as I once was. Why would I not accept them into my practice? What was being a doctor all about, anyway?

There were only two stipulations I had for accepting new patients, and both concerned demonstrating the same respect for me as I had for them. The first was that patients had to pay something to demonstrate a responsibility for their own care. I was more than willing to make accommodations for those in tough financial straights, but there were those people who would see a doctor numerous times, and always have some excuse at each visit for not being able to pay. It was deplorable. I gave Maureen wide latitude to adjust bills for patients who could not afford my full office fee, but I always insisted that they made some amount of payment.

My second rule for new patients was that they had to arrive at my office clean. It was completely understandable for a patient to arrive sweaty, disheveled or unwashed in an emergency situation. But if an advance appointment was made, I thought it inexcusable not to have at least bathed. Lady Liberty on Ellis Island welcomed the poor, huddled masses. Once here, however, soap and water were plentiful.

Eventually, my hospital census grew, as did the volume of patients I saw in my office. I no longer needed the supplemental income, so I was able to resign from my part-time industrial jobs to concentrate on my private practice. I did, however, maintain my half-time position at the hospital.

One valuable source of new patients turned out to be Maureen herself. Once we got to know each other, she began referring her neighbors. It wasn't long before it felt like I was treating half of the population of Woodside. Nor was it long before Maureen asked me to see members of her family. There were upsides and downsides to doing so. While I was happy for the additions to my practice, I was concerned that if problems arose, they could sour my relationship with Maureen, and I really did not want that to happen. She was a boon to my practice. But considering what a good-natured woman Maureen was, I figured her family would be the same, and I elected to take the chance.

Uncle Sean, her mother's brother, was an easygoing gentleman in his fifties, a gregarious storyteller, and a character right out of a Damon Runyon novel. Sean liked to drink. He'd sit at the end of a bar and regale anyone who would listen with tales of his exploits. The problem was that Sean had no real exploits to brag about. He lived in a world of his own making. He'd tell stories of sales that he made, of deals he had brokered and of travels to far away places. They were all concocted; he never had a meaningful job, ever.

At his first visit, we established that he had been a drinker for the better part of his life, and that he had once been hospitalized for pancreatitis. I urged Sean to stop drinking. Another episode of pancreatitis, I told him, could kill him. I recommended he go to Alcoholics Anonymous for support.

"Nah, Doc, no way. I'll quit, but I'm not going to no A.A. meeting with those derelicts and misfits."

Sean's answer for abstinence was to substitute drugs for alcohol. It began with marijuana. A joint gave him a high like a martini. It wasn't the high he was looking for, so he soon graduated to heroin. He injected himself on a regular basis. He rationalized that, as long as he wasn't "mainlining," he wasn't a degenerate addict.

Sean had no trouble telling me what he did. To him it was like going to confession, and he seemed to feel a sense of relief whenever he confessed to me what he had done. I never learned where he got the money to support his habit. Whenever I asked, he would just smile and change the subject. He lived alone, and as far as I knew, he did not have a girlfriend. The only girls in his life were the ones he met up with at bars.

Sean's injection site of choice was the quadriceps muscle of his thighs. Not being the most meticulous man I ever met, Lord only knows how dirty were his syringes and needles, and Sean would often come to me with infected needle holes and abscesses. Over time, Sean's thigh muscles became hard as a rock. He could barely walk. He stumbled and lurched about, unable to fully straighten his legs or bend them at the knee. I was uncertain as to the cause of the stiffness, so I ordered an X-ray. To my surprise, there were extensive calcifications in both of Sean's quadriceps muscles, a condition called *myositis ossificans*. In essence, his muscles had turned into bone.

The most common cause of *myositis ossificans* is repeated trauma. I will never forget the X-rays of a running back who played football for the New York Giants who developed the condition from being repeatedly tackled on the gridiron. The film showed his quadriceps muscle was entirely stippled with flecks of calcium. It looked like the Milky Way.

Sean and I had many, many conversations about his life. He told me stories that he thought would be entertaining. At the end of each tale, he'd give me a wink, suggesting that everything he had just said may or may not have been true. He would promise to get a handle on his life, to refrain from drug use, and to get a job. It was all blarney. He knew it. I knew it. But he was affable and gregarious and had a way of making me believe he meant it. Until the next time he came to see me with blood and pus oozing from an injection site in his thigh.

It seemed that Sean was resigned to living his life as he was. It was never his intention to quit. He would sit in front of me, sheepish and apologetic. He was twenty years older than I, but looked at me as if he expected me to reprimand or scold him. The man just couldn't help himself. No matter how hard he said he tried to straighten out his life, he would behave like an errant child awaiting punishment whenever he strayed. It went on like this for the nine years he remained my patient, until he was ultimately found dead in bed in his apartment.

Curiously, his family only seemed to be upset by Sean's physical problems, not with the fact that he was an addict. They treated him like a pet, like a lovable dog that had defecated on the rug. Their ever-present sentiment was "Oh well! That's Sean for ya!" It was a difficult attitude to observe, this resignation to a loved one's self-destruction, but it was one that I recognized, having had my own experience watching someone descend into debilitating addiction.

My roommate in college was a handsome Irishman who stood six feet two inches tall, had a square-jaw and perfectly aligned teeth, blond hair and deep, sea-blue eyes. Joe was an athlete. He was no ordinary tennis player; he was seeded high up in ranking among high schools. When he entered Holy Cross College, he was immediately named captain of the tennis team. During summer breaks, he taught tennis at several prominent Westchester country clubs and earned a considerable amount of money. There was only one problem with his storybook life: Joe liked to drink.

Beer, mostly.

Beer, considerably.

Beer, often.

The night before any tennis match at school, Joe would sneak off campus to the local gin mill and get totally smashed. In our day, we had curfew of 11:30 p.m. No one was allowed off campus for any reason whatsoever. I never knew when or how he returned to our room (I slept the sleep of the dead), but the next morning, Joe would show up promptly at the courts, take his warm up practice volleys and serves, stand ready to play, and then turn, vomit profusely, and walk off the court. It didn't happen once. It happened more often than not.

In the interim between tournaments, Joe's behavior remained the same. He'd sneak off campus, get drunk, return to our room, and in the middle of the night, fall out of bed. If I heard the thud of his body hitting the floor, I would somehow pick him up and struggle to get him back into the bed. He would just fall out again. After several months of that routine, I came to an existential conclusion: No one falls off the floor! I just covered him with a blanket and let him lie there. In the morning he would thank me for being so considerate.

Upon graduation, I went off to medical school and he got a job selling advertising space for a national magazine. He married his childhood sweetheart, and in short order the babies came tumbling out. In eight short years he had six children. He had a Victorian home in one of Westchester County's more affluent suburbs. His job necessitated that he entertain clients. It's a common expression that executives sometimes enjoy a "two-martini lunch." For Joe, they were starters. He drank at lunch, he drank at dinner, and he drank into the night. He commuted to and from his office in Manhattan on the New York Central line from Grand Central Station. Across the street from the railroad station was the Roosevelt Hotel. Joe was a fixture at the bar from quitting time to when he could no longer make excuses for not going home.

We met from time to time for lunch. We were working in totally different worlds, but shared the bond of having lived together for three years. He would regale me with stories of his business accomplishments, and I'd tell him about my travails of starting a medical practice. I was still a nominal practicing Catholic, but Joe was at the extreme end of religiosity. He would go on and on about losing one's immortal soul, the need for redemption, the necessity of confession (as if any behavior was acceptable so long as a confessional was nearby to gain absolution.) Needless to say, the lunches were not exhilarating.

Joe's marriage went south. Since he was no longer enjoying connubial bliss with his wife, he began to seek sex elsewhere, typically with someone he met at the Roosevelt Hotel bar. That's when the phone calls began. Joe would call me from some cheap hotel room. He'd have no idea where he was. He'd have no idea with whom he had spent the night. He'd be terrified. He'd ask me to wire him some money so he could get a cab and go home. He came to see me several times with scabies, a parasitic infestation of the pubic hairs. The treatment was simple but the cause was so much more complex. It spoke of unseemliness. It spoke of degradation. I appealed to his religiosity, to obtain forgiveness, to straighten out his life if for no other reason than for his six children. My entreaties and exhortations fell on deaf ears.

Several years later, Joe got into an automobile accident while he was intoxicated, and suffered several fractured bones, including his pelvis. The injuries necessitated a long hospital stay, during which he called me many times. Invariably, he'd call during office hours, never at night when I was freer to talk, so the conversations were somewhat abrupt. We reprised the conversations of the past, but this time he was sober, and I believed he was listening.

The magazine he worked for could no longer put up with his behavior, despite his continuing accomplishments. He was, in fact, a consummate salesman, but the magazine no longer wished to endure his absences and the rumors that swirled around the circle of publishers. The magazine bought out his employment contract with a generous settlement, and Joe sought employment with a smaller, local magazine.

Then the miraculous happened. Joe found Alcoholics Anonymous. Not only did he sober up, he became a champion for the organization. He'd go out in the middle of the night to rescue someone who had fallen off the wagon. He'd spend hours with an individual who desperately needed a drink and was afraid to be alone for fear of having that drink. He approached classmates he knew who were having trouble with alcohol and encouraged them to join A.A. He became messianic. He could talk of nothing else. As addicted as he was to alcohol, he was now as consumed with promoting A.A. It was a remarkable transformation.

Joe divorced his wife of twenty-five years. It turned out that she drank more than he did. He told me he had to do it in order to stay sober. He could not be in her company without seeing her under the influence. He could not enter his home without seeing the trappings of her alcoholism. It caused him no end of grief. He sat on the horns of a dilemma: he was a good, practicing Catholic, so divorce was not in his lexicon, yet his wife refused to admit her problem or to join with him in the program.

Ultimately, Joe moved to Florida, as far away from her as he could and still be available to his children. He remained sober for the rest of his life. Whenever I spoke with him, he would remind me how many years and days he had maintained sobriety. He remained a champion for A.A. He remarried in his last days, to a woman who loved him like no other.

Understanding the genesis of alcoholism is no easy task. I always though that Joe diminished himself so he would not eclipse or outshine his older, less gifted brother. It was a simplistic notion on my part. As an internist, I could only deal with the aftermath. Psychiatrists have trouble understanding it. It remains an enigmatic disease.

Sleuth

The clergy get sick like everyone else.

It was commonly understood that the nuns at St. Vincent's lived on a very modest stipend. When I began my practice, I had overheard several senior physicians whisper that they didn't much like taking care of the nuns. They found it awkward to bill them, but neither did they want to provide services without compensation. So, some of my colleagues went out of their way to discourage clergy from entering their already established practices, and instead referred them to fledgling doctors like myself, whom they assumed would be flattered to accept the referral.

What I quickly learned was that members of the clergy may not have been wealthy, but many were eligible for Medicare, and the remainder had spectacular medical insurance. This seems to have gone unnoticed by many of my colleagues, who often wondered how or why a physician such as I would be willing to care for so many clergy. On one occasion in the doctor's lounge, one green-eyed dope of a physician cornered me.

"So, Vic," he condescended, "how can you handle so many clergy on the cuff?"

"I never bill them," I said, watching him smirk and look at me like I was a fool. "But I do bill their insurance carrier."

The look of bewilderment on his face spoke volumes.

In my practice, I never touched money. I purposely never accepted payment in my consultation room (or anywhere else for that matter). I wanted always to keep medicine separate from money. Patients came to see me for their problems, and they settled the finances with my secretary. One elderly lady came into my consultation room to settle her hospital bill. She began to count out five and ten dollar bills onto my desk. I stopped her, insisting she see my secretary.

"She gonna steal-a da money," she pleaded.

"No, no, Mrs. Sammartino, she's very honest."

"I hope you no make-a mistake," Mrs. Sammartino warned me, wagging her bony finger in my direction.

Sister Eileen came to me on the advice of Sister McOwen, who oversaw the hospital laboratories. I can only assume that Sister McOwen's referral came because of my association with Carol, which gave me at least as much credence with her as a doctor as Carol had as a chemist. I knew Sister Eileen. We met when I did a six month surgical rotation during my internship. At the time, I looked at her with awe. She had a very responsible position overseeing all of the operating rooms in the hospital. They were in constant use, day and night, and keeping them properly staffed was a demanding and nerve-wracking job.

At her first visit with me, she had few complaints. She mainly wanted to establish a relationship. Sister was a large woman. I would not categorize her as obese, but she had a huge physical frame. My only substantive finding on that first visit was that she had a slightly elevated blood pressure. I discreetly tried to suggest she lose some weight, but it fell on deaf ears.

As my professional relationship with Sister Eileen grew, we became friends. I met her brother when he invited me to visit him on the floor of the American Stock Exchange, where he worked. He was also a big man, but seemed to carry his weight well. Later, I chanced to meet Sister in front of the nurses' residence, where she introduced me to her mother. Their bodies were interchangeable. On the spot, I mentally abandoned any further attempt to encourage her to lose weight. Clearly, there was a genetic component to her size, and slavishly treating a number on a dial was not the same as treating a patient.

It was in early spring one year when Sister complained that she had begun to wheeze and cough. She also developed a mild shortness of breath, which I attributed to her carrying around the extra pounds. I had no idea why a mature woman would suddenly develop asthma, but I treated her for it, and by fall her symptoms improved. By winter they had abated completely, and we were content that it had been just "one of those things" that befall us from time to time. But once spring came around again, so did her asthma.

It was a recurring cycle. Every year she was treated in the same way. Her symptoms abated with treatment, but each subsequent year they worsened. Her asthma significantly interfered with her ability to perform as the supervisor of the operating room. By the spring of the fourth year, she was desperately ill. Sister was gasping for breath, and her wheeze could be heard without a stethoscope. She could not be cared for alone in her convent room. I had no alternative but to admit her to the hospital.

Tests indicated that Sister was in serious trouble. The level of oxygen in her blood was well below normal. She did not respond to hydration or supplemental oxygen, nor did the usual cocktail of medicines for asthma have any substantial effect. She did not respond to bronchodilators. I decided to prescribe cortisone.

Cortisone had only been on the market for a little more than a decade. In my opinion, it is one of the most significant additions to Medicine next to insulin and penicillin. The anti-inflammatory action of supplemental cortisone changed the way many diseases are treated. The amount that can be administered is significantly more than the body can produce on its own, and thus can virtually shut down the immune (allergic) system. The results were breathtaking. However, we were just beginning to learn that long-term usage of this "miracle drug" had the deleterious effect of causing cataracts, diabetes, aseptic necrosis of the hip, or osteoporosis. But for short term use, it did so much good that the trade-off was justified. Besides, knowing the risks and hazards of overuse put one on notice not to abuse the drug.

The Chief of Pediatrics at St. Vincent's, Dr. David Esposito, happened to be the Cardinal's personal physician. It is not quite clear why a pediatrician attended a Prince of the Church, but it was rumored that his appointment to Chief was influenced by that relationship. Dr. Esposito also co-authored the seminal paper for diagnosing child abuse. (Actually, a medical school classmate of mine discovered classic findings on X-ray that can only be explained by abuse, and he wrote the paper while doing his residency training in pediatrics.) Having the lead article in the New England Journal of Medicine and having a direct connection to the Cardinal led Dr. Esposito to believe he had more authority than he actually had.

He absolutely forbade the use of cortisone for children on the pediatric service. (He was probably right to do so, as young children are far more susceptible to the harmful effects of the drug.) However, he believed his departmental mandate applied to all physicians in the hospital.

Somehow, Dr. Esposito got wind that I was caring for Sister Eileen. He also learned that I had started her on high doses of cortisone. He was furious. He confronted me at the nurses' station outside of Sister Eileen's room.

"How dare you prescribe cortisone?" he demanded.

"I'm sorry, I didn't get the memo," I replied. "When did you become Chief of Medicine?"

Who the hell does this guy think he is?! I thought.

"Don't you know the side effects of cortisone?" he sneered, running is fingers through his bleached blond hair.

"I do. And I also know that adults can die from asthma."

"I forbid you to prescribe cortisone," he screamed.

"Fuck you, David! I've been Sister's doctor for over four years. Until she dismisses me and engages you, she will remain on exactly what I prescribe for her. Are we clear?"

Needless to say, we never established a cordial relationship.

The cortisone was effective. Sister recovered from her bout of asthma. I suggested she take some time off before she resumed her duties, and she took my advice. Upon her return, I stopped by her office to see how she was settling back in. For all the years I cared for Sister Eileen, I only saw her in my office, in the operating suite, or in various public areas of the hospital. This was my first visit to her office, which was a small space on the third floor of the Raskob Building. It overlooked the central courtyard, but the window was level with the roof of the adjacent chapel. Wedged in the lower sash of the window was an air conditioner.

The original hospital building was constructed in the late nineteenth century, long before air conditioning was even envisioned. All subsequent hospital buildings were also absent central air (which made for some murderous summer days when, for example, hospital administrators refused to allow any windows in the emergency room to be opened, for issues of "privacy.") The only air conditioned areas were the operating rooms and a few laboratories. By virtue of her position, however, Sister Eileen was able to obtain one for herself.

I looked out the window to find that all manner of debris had collected on the rooftop under the unit during the winter.

"Sister," I asked, "would you mind if I opened this air conditioner?"

She looked at me quizzically. "Why would you want to?"

"It's just a hunch, Sister," I said with a bit of a wry smile.

When I took to checking the air conditioner's filter, I discovered that it had probably never been cleaned in all the years it had been used. It was caked with dust, debris and dirt.

In an instant, it all became clear. Sister Eileen was allergic to mold spores. Every spring, with the rise in temperature, Sister turned on her air conditioner. Soon after, she began to wheeze, never associating the symptom with its cause.

Unfortunately, there were no blood tests to prove my hypothesis, and Sister refused to undergo scratch testing, a tedious process of applying known allergens to a scratch on the back to see if a reaction occurred. However, merely cleaning out her air conditioner and having the roof swept solved her asthmatic problem.

It's amazing what one can learn simply by visiting a patient's home or work place.

House Calls

The image of doctors making house calls has been relegated to a Norman Rockwell painting: a nostalgic relic of times past. We imagine a kindly, grey-bearded man ambling down the road—medical bag in hand, stethoscope at the ready—off to visit his bed-ridden patient, who is just too sick and too weak to travel to his office. We romanticize picturesque bedside care, where the pillows are fluffed just so, and the doting family waits just outside the door for the good doctor's advice.

Though mostly a custom long ago abandoned (and rarely so beatific), there was a time when house calls were part and parcel of a physician's practice.

Angelo Molina was one of my very first patients. He came to me complaining of excruciating pain in his legs. He could barely walk a quarter of a block without experiencing painful cramps in his calf muscles. Upon examination I found that his feet were cold, and I could not discern a pulse below his femoral artery. Angelo had an arterial blockage, even though he had no risk factors for arteriosclerosis other than being a long-time smoker. Unfortunately, femoral artery bypass surgery was virtually non-existent at the time; very few surgeons attempted it and artificial graft material had yet to be invented. Angelo's lower extremities were in jeopardy. He visited me regularly for check ups, and we got to know each other over the course of the next several months.

Angelo was a bartender who lived in SoHo, the area south of Houston Street. He lived in the same neighborhood in which he was born and raised. He attended our Lady of Pompeii, and because of his long-time association with the church, was an active participant in the Feast of San Gennaro, the annual celebration of the Patron Saint of Naples. Every September, the festival begins with the statue of San Gennaro carried on the shoulders of several burly men on a mile-long religious procession along Mulberry and Mott Streets in Little Italy, and ends with a multi-day street fair and celebration. The feast was the battery that energized Angelo's life. His inability to walk severely compromised his involvement, and it saddened him terribly.

After a year of follow up, Angelo's legs below the knee had turned purple, and his small toes were turning black. There was no way to save his legs. His only recourse was "above the knee" amputations, which would severely limit his mobility, relegating him to a wheelchair for the remainder of his life.

Angelo had the surgery and returned to his home to convalesce. After several weeks, I made a house call. He lived on the corner of Sullivan and Houston Streets, about ten blocks from my office. Of course, his apartment was on the top floor of a four-floor walk-up apartment building. Reaching his door only slightly winded from the climb, I was cordially greeted by Angelo's wife and ushered in. Angelo and I exchanged pleasantries, but it was clear to me from the tenor and tone of the conversation that Angelo was depressed. He certainly had every right to be. Losing one leg is tragic. Losing both at once is cataclysmic.

When I got to examine Angelo, I found the wounds to be healing nicely. He showed me how he could transfer from his bed to a wheelchair, and seemed proud of his achievement. He said he was making every effort to adjust to his new life, but I somehow sensed it was a lie.

About three weeks later, I walked into my office and was flabbergasted to find Angelo in the waiting room, sitting in a wheelchair. When it was his turn to see me, my first question to him was "How the hell did you get down four flights of stairs?"

"I wiggled down on my ass one step at a time."

I was baffled. The staircase was cast iron with marble saddles. Every landing was cold inlaid tile.

"I just rocked from one cheek to the other and, in no time, I reached the lobby."

"Well," I said, "getting down is one thing, but how are you going to get back up?"

"Don't worry, I got friends in the neighborhood.

"That's a lot to ask of friends, isn't it?" I said.

"Hey Doc, if they can carry the statue of San Gennaro around all day, they can carry me up the stairs once in a while."

I looked at Angelo long and hard. Maybe he wasn't as depressed as I had thought.

"Don't push your luck. I'll come to you."

I went to see him as often as necessary. Angelo always insisted that he pay for my house call while I was there. He paid with cash, a nice custom among the Italians.

There was simplicity to making house calls. It was much easier, and far more efficient, for me to walk a few blocks to see Angelo in his apartment than it would have been for Angelo to arrange an ambulance service to transport him for a routine check-up. I charged what I normally charged for an office visit, plus a small premium for the extra time required. It was a far cry from the fee Angelo would be charged for the ambulance and its two attendants. With the advent of Medicare, however, simplicity (and logic) slowly became a thing of the past.

*****

Medicine had always been a fee for service profession. When I started practice, I charged ten dollars for an office visit. If a patient came to see me and didn't have health insurance, they would pay out of pocket. Often times, my colleagues and I would accept payment on a "sliding scale" to benefit those we knew to be financially struggling. More often than not, those struggling patients were the elderly, who had reached a point in their lives when they no longer had the financial means to maintain an indemnity policy for themselves. Enter Medicare.

Medicare came into being on July 1, 1966 (coincidentally the same day I went into practice) to guarantee that the elderly had suitable insurance. Blue Cross/Blue Shield of New York serviced Medicare claims. They reimbursed physicians eighty percent of "prevailing and customary" fees. Upon submission of a completed form, I would receive a check for eight dollars, often in the return mail. Blue Cross was quite efficient that way. It was left to me to collect the remaining two dollars from my patient. For the indigent, I chose not to pursue it.

I had been working with Dr. De Bellis for a couple of years when he asked me one day to make a house call for him. The patient lived on Fifth Avenue and 15th Street. It was only six short blocks north of the office, but Hannibal was suffering from serious lung disease and he was constantly short of breath. To him, those six blocks were more like six miles. I obliged, and as I headed to the door, he called out to me, "Make sure he pays you before you leave!"

A curious piece of advice, I thought, but having been well-served by his idea to pack my waiting room, I wasn't about to question him. Perhaps this patient had a history of nonpayment, and Hannibal was looking out for me.

I arrived at the apartment and introduced myself to a man who looked to be in his eighties. Mr. Chapman was a most charming man, slight of build and impeccably dressed. His apartment was replete with fine furniture and oriental rugs. It reeked of affluence.

Mr. Chapman complained of shortness of breath. He was suffering from mitral stenosis, a severely narrowed valve in his heart. He was too old to consider open-heart surgery. The most that could be offered to him was a "finger fracture" of the narrowed valve, which was a procedure employed only in desperate situations, and in most cases provided results that were less than satisfactory. On this day, however, Mr. Chapman was only looking for reassurance that his condition was not worsening.

During my visit, I asked him what he had done for a living. He pointed to the window. Across the street was a building with "Annin Flag" carved in the stone crown. Mr. Chapman owned one of the most prestigious American flag manufacturers in the country, and talked at length about the many special flags his company produced for the United States government. He had long since stopped running the company, but he rented an apartment across the street from his building so that he could be near to it.

I was in awe. I was charmed. I felt foolish asking him for money. But Hannibal had insisted. As discretely as I could, I suggested that it was preferable for my fee to be paid then and there, rather than sending a bill. Mr. Chapman smiled at me, took money from his pocket, peeled off some bills and said, "Hannibal put you up to this, didn't he?"

I never did figure it out. Given his history and surroundings, it was unlikely that Mr. Chapman was the kind of man who didn't pay his bills. Besides, at his age he certainly qualified for Medicare, so getting reimbursed shouldn't have been a problem. Perhaps it was just a private joke between Dr. De Bellis and Mr. Chapman. Regardless, my face must have been crimson.

*****

Jim Ianelli, a resident physician at St. Vincent's, approached me one day and asked if I would make a house call on his uncle. I was rather flattered that he asked me out of the hundreds of practicing physicians at the hospital. It was impossible to say no. After learning that his uncle Giuseppe lived down in Chinatown, however, I began to have second thoughts. This was not a quick trip from the hospital or my home. It would require a subway ride and a hefty walk to get there.

Nevertheless, I went on the call after I completed office hours that evening. Giuseppe Ianelli lived in a walkup east of the Bowery and south of the Manhattan Bridge. His wife greeted me at the door. She spoke little English and mumbled a lot in Italian. I gathered that her husband was quite ill, and sensed from the urgency of her speech that she was frantic about it. She led me to the bedroom, in which a large man lay in a bed too small for his frame. He was delirious and could offer me no meaningful information. I took his temperature and was shocked to read 105 degrees on my mercury thermometer. I examined him as best I could in the dark apartment, listening to his lungs, listening to his heart, and palpating his abdomen. The examination was less than perfect, but with a raging fever of that magnitude and delirium setting in, there was but one option: get him to a hospital. As I went to call for an ambulance, Mrs. Ianelli grabbed my arm.

"St. Vincent?" she asked.

"No, Ma'am. The ambulance will come from Gouverneur hospital."

"No. St. Vincent," she said with finality. "With Giacomo."

Clearly, she wanted her husband where his nephew could oversee his care. We had to arrange for a private ambulance. We waited for an eternity for it to arrive.

Once admitted to the hospital, the preliminary blood tests confirmed the presence of a raging infection. His white blood count was through the roof. Cultures showed the presence of Staphylococcus aureus, but the patient had no wounds on his skin to account for the source of the infection. He was treated with massive doses of antibiotics, but to no avail. Even in the early 1970s, many strains of the bacteria were resistant to penicillin and other antibiotics. The man drifted into septic shock and died of overwhelming sepsis.

The autopsy revealed an abscess in the patient's heart. Even if we had known of its existence, it would not have mattered. It wasn't the kind of thing one could lance or excise. The man had a fulminant disease at the outset and was destined to die, but the family was forever grateful that I came to their home to try to save his life. That he had received care in a hospital where his nephew was involved was therapeutic in and of itself.

When I submitted paperwork to Medicare for Mr. Ianelli's, however, I ran into a bureaucratic problem: they only reimbursed house calls at the prevailing rate of an office visit. My fee of twenty dollars was rejected (I had, by this point, raised my base office fee to fifteen dollars). Medicare had unilaterally decided that they would make no accommodation for the additional time a doctor invested to make a house call. The other insurance companies quickly followed suit. The fact that I had travelled to the patient's home, spent several hours caring for him, waiting for an ambulance, and accompanying him to the hospital mattered not at all. My fee received the same dispatch as one for seeing someone in my office with the common cold. I received a check for twelve dollars. It made no sense. All appeals to Blue Cross/Blue Shield were met with the same disinterest.

"That's the way it's coded, Doctor."

*****

When I first met Carol, she was the supervisor of the chemistry laboratory. Sister McOwen was her superior. For all the years I was a resident physician, Sister and I had a singularly professional relationship. Our conversations were all business. We shared nothing of a personal nature. Sister was a phlegmatic woman who rarely displayed emotion, whether in her voice, facial expression, or body language. When she heard of Carol's and my engagement, I am told she was very happy, but in my imagination I can only see her staring blankly at Carol, announcing in an affectless and unconvincing monotone, "I'm thrilled."

One day in the middle of morning rounds, Sister buttonholed me in the hallway and asked if I would make a house call.

"On whom?" I asked.

"My sister," she replied without a trace of concern. Then she added as an afterthought, "Moira."

I had no idea how urgent the request was or even where Eileen lived. However, Sister McOwen was my wife's boss, and I surely did not want to jeopardize that relationship in any way. I figured I had better suck it up and do the right thing.

"Of course," I said. "Where does you sister live?" I asked with a bit of trepidation. For all I knew, Moira lived somewhere up in the Bronx.

"She has an apartment on West Twelfth Street, number fifteen."

I knew the building well. It was just off of Fifth Avenue, across the street from the First Presbyterian Church. Several physicians from St. Vincent's conducted their practice in the ground floor apartments. Although relieved that I did not have to trek to a distant borough, I wondered why she didn't ask one of them.

"Can we go right away, Doctor? I have the key."

That was strange. Why couldn't her sister open her door like anyone else? Was she that incapacitated? And if she were, why wouldn't Sister bring her to the hospital?

We walked out of the main entrance of the hospital and headed east. We had a surprisingly pleasant chat, at first talking about nothing important or anything pertaining to the hospital. We paused in front of the New School for Social Research, and marveled at how rapidly it had grown in size and stature. It didn't rival New York University, but it was becoming a force unto itself. I remarked to Sister that Carol was enrolled in a course in computer science to learn how to integrate the newly invented automated laboratory systems with the mainframe computer.

"We were happy to pay her tuition," she said.

"Oh, so you're the reason my dinner is always late."

Sister tried to laugh. "Your wife is a treasure," she said.

"Don't I know it."

We passed the vacant lot where the anarchist group, the Weathermen, had accidentally blown up a townhouse while attempting to make bombs. We just shook our heads. The emptiness required no comment from either of us.

Then, out of the clear blue, Sister asked, "When are you two planning to start a family?"

"It's not for lack of trying."

Sister gave me a wry smile, and we walked on.

At the apartment house, the doorman waved us to the elevator. We arrived at the apartment door and Sister opened it with a key she produced from one of the capacious pockets in the skirt of her habit. There, seated on the couch in the living room, was Moira.

She was stone cold dead.

It was a startling tableau. She was stiff as a board. Beside her body were partially consumed bottles of alcohol. Several empty bottles, each a different brand, were strewn on the floor around her. Old, crumpled newspapers littered every surface in the room, and an overturned ashtray on the coffee table left a pile of cigarette butts at her feet. The room was dark and the air felt thick. It reeked of body odor, alcohol and cigarettes.

New York State law stipulated that a body could not be moved unless it was officially pronounced dead by a licensed physician. During my internship, it was incumbent to "ride the ambulance," and go out on calls all across the city to pronounce victims dead so the body could be taken to the morgue. Many cases were grotesque. There was a man who jumped from the eightieth floor of the Empire State Building and landed on the Thirty-Fourth Street sidewalk. What remained of him—something resembling a sack of straw—was covered in a tarpaulin. (In my naïveté, I actually knelt down to check for a pulse. The police around me snickered.) No intern I knew could forget the bodies fished out of the Hudson River. The sight and smell of such corpses are indelible. Then there were the subway jumpers. Climbing down from the platform onto the train tracks and crawling under a motionless subway car to reach a dismembered body is something I wish I could forget. Neither do I like to dwell on having had to sign the death certificate of a victim of hydrocephalus, one of nature's grotesqueries. His head was so large and his body so disproportionately small that I could not imagine him ever having held his own head up in all the fourteen short years of his life.

But for all of the people I pronounced, never before had I come across a corpse sitting bolt upright on a couch. How had she not slumped over onto the seat cushions or fallen to the floor? I went through the formality of the ritual to confirm that Moira was indeed dead, and turned to Sister to deliver what I thought would be shocking news. Her reaction was curious; she took it too well. News of her sister's demise came as no surprise to her. I began to suspect that she must have already known that Eileen succumbed before we arrived at the apartment, before she even requested my services, and that there was another reason for my presence here.

When a death occurs without a doctor in attendance, the police must be notified. Police officers who arrive on the scene are then obligated to notify the Medical Examiner and call for an ambulance. The intern riding the ambulance pronounced the person dead (allowing for the removal of the body), and provided a probable cause of death. Depending on the circumstances, the Medical Examiner may call for the body to perform an autopsy, or else accept the intern's diagnosis and release the body to an undertaker. In either case, before the body could be buried, the State required that a licensed physician sign a death certificate.

If I were to sign a death certificate with a plausible diagnosis, Sister knew she could avoid that circus. She also knew I was one to respect her privacy, and not feed the gossip mill with news that her sister had died or (probably more importantly to her) that alcoholism contributed to her sister's death. Perhaps she knew intuitively, or perhaps she learned through Carol that I knew when to keep my mouth shut. Clearly, she was ashamed that alcoholism had so ravaged her sibling.

I did not submit a bill for the house call. When one lives and works in a tight knit community, some services are courtesy.

Besides, how would I have "coded" it?

*****

Rosalind Epstein lived in my apartment building with her husband, Ed. They were the salt of the earth, the gentlest of people. They were childless, and at the time, so were we. We visited each other often, sharing local gossip over cocktails. Roz was a secretary and Ed worked at a company that fabricated envelopes. I had no idea there were so many kinds of envelopes until Ed educated me on the nuances of the business. Ed was a collector. In their one-bedroom apartment, he had perhaps two hundred miniature bottles of alcohol. There were bottles everywhere: on shelves, on tables, and in cupboards. Ed regaled us with stories of where he had acquired them. It was one of the most unusual collections I had ever seen.

Roz came to see me regularly for routine check ups. On one of her visits, I detected a lump in her breast by palpation, and confirmed it by mammography. Radical mastectomy was the standard treatment, but Rosalind would have none of it. She had large breasts, and the thought of a disfiguring mastectomy was dismissed out of hand.

After some research and due diligence, I found several reports in the medical literature that indicated lumpectomy was equally as effective as radical mastectomy. Although all of the surgeons at my hospital considered these reports heresy, I managed to convince one to perform the procedure for Roz.

Several days after surgery, Roz called my office to say that she was severely constipated. She was more than uncomfortable; she was in agony. Could she come see me immediately? I told her that there wasn't much I could do for her in my office, but that I'd be happy to stop by her apartment to see what was the matter.

Rosalind had a fecal impaction, an uncomplicated yet embarrassing problem. I took her to the bathroom, and as I pulled on a latex glove, I explained to her that she had a stone-hard lump of feces in her rectum that was far too large for her to expel. I would have to remove it manually. Standing toe to toe in the tiny room, she looked at me squarely in the eye, unflinching.

"Vic, I don't give a shit what you have to do."

I held her gaze, trying not to smirk. After all, she was desperate. When she finally realized what she had said, Roz was the first to crack, and we both burst into uncontrollable laughter. I can't imagine what Ed must have thought was happening in their bathroom.

It was a simple, if unglamorous, diagnosis and remedy. It took me all of a couple of minutes to relieve days of suffering. However, had I been in practice today and subjected to the policies and the dictates of the insurance companies, I would have had to send Roz to the emergency room. There, despite her problem being obvious, she undoubtedly would have had blood drawn for tests and had an X-ray taken of her abdomen. A radiologist would have to read the X-ray (at a separate fee), and an intern would be summoned to address the impaction. Unaware of her clinical background, she likely would be advised to have a colonoscopy as well.

And yet, we endure this nonsense because the insurance companies refused to pay five extra dollars for a house call.

Carol

"Unfortunately, Carol, there is no specific test for Parkinson's disease. We can only make a diagnosis based on a triad of symptoms. There has to be tremor, rigidity, and postural instability." Sitting at his desk, William Doherty continued to explain the signs and symptoms of Parkinson's to Carol. "What you are calling 'a twitch' is really evidence of a tremor, a pin rolling of your hand. But tremor alone can be caused by any number of things. But you also complain of stiffness, feeling your muscles are 'weighted down,' and I detected a particular rigidity in your muscles that we call cog-wheeling."

"What does that mean, Bill?" she asked.

"Carol," Dr. Doherty concluded, "right now, you're exhibiting two of the three telltale signs. I'm comfortable in confirming that it probably is Parkinson's. Fortunately, you have no evidence of postural instability, yet."

"What is that?"

"Patients with Parkinson's lose their ability to stand and walk without support. You lose your ability to balance. So, if you were standing up, and I gave you a nudge, your brain wouldn't register the spatial change, and you might topple over. You'll always know where your feet are, but you'll have trouble controlling them." Carol sat in total silence, absorbing the implication of what he said. "But Carol, please don't concern yourself with that now. You are still in the early stages of the disease, and it will likely be many years before you require medical intervention."

"You think so?" Carol looked up and met Dr. Doherty's eyes. It was the first ray of emotion she had displayed the entire visit.

"Yes. Your tremor is still slight and your rigidity is mild. Parkinson's is not generally known for rapid progression. We'll continue to monitor you and the disease's advancement, but for right now, I recommend that you go home and live your life, OK?"

"OK." Carol gave him a weak smile, stood up and shook his hand. "Thank you very much, Doctor."

"Thanks, Bill," I said, shaking his hand and patting his shoulder, grateful for the clarity and kindness with which he had explained Carol's disease to her. "We'll be in touch."

Carol and I returned home and attempted to resume our usual routine. Life settled back into a semblance of normalcy, but we avoided the topic of her disease at all costs. If anyone ever made reference to the movement in her hand, Carol was quick to say, "I have a pinched nerve in my neck."

"Oh, you poor thing!" was a reply typically spoken by a friend or loved one duped into the idea that the twitch was an inconvenient symptom of arthritis.

I was forbidden to elaborate. In fact, I was mandated to keep silent.

"My parents can't ever know," Carol implored me.

"Carol, don't be ridiculous. They're your parents! They are going to know sooner or later. Wouldn't it help to have their support?"

She went quiet for a while, and then whispered, "Don't you understand? My aunt is on her way to a nursing home with Parkinson's. If my parents knew what was wrong with me, it would kill them."

What could I say? I could appreciate Carol's desire to insulate her parents. It's a natural impulse to want to shield loved ones from hardship. But Carol and I both come from very close-knit (and talkative) families, and in order to ensure that word didn't reach her parents, she decided we could tell no one the truth. For years we lived a lie, telling anyone who asked that it was a pinched nerve in her neck that caused the tremor in her hand. With Carol's history of neck and back problems, people believed it. Or, rather, they chose to believe it.

From the early days of our marriage, when we lived in Manhattan, Carol and I long had the habit of going for walks together after dinner. It didn't matter what the season, we'd escape the cramped quarters of our one-bedroom apartment for a few hours each night by walking around our neighborhood. We'd examine every window of every store and shop we passed. We'd study the people around us, how they dressed, how they conducted themselves. We'd whisper to each other who we thought was better groomed, or who wore the nicer jewelry. We'd walk in fair weather and in the rain, but the walks in the snow were our favorites. They invariably ended with a snowball fight. (I won't divulge who won.)

After we moved to the suburbs, we continued our habit of walking our neighborhood. Shops and windows were replaced by trees and lawns, and our commentary was limited to who did a better job maintaining their yard. But it was a peaceful village where we lived, and the snow in winter was more conducive to throwing at each other.

We always held hands. What had once been merely a sign of affection between us now seemed a necessity for Carol to maintain her balance. On one quiet walk, spent with virtually no conversation, she suddenly turned to me and said, "You know, you'll have to do all the cooking."

When I was in practice, I often marveled at how my patients reacted to a diagnosis, whether one as simple as tonsillitis or devastating as cancer. It seemed that the subconscious somehow came to the fore at such stressful moments. For Carol, some of her proudest moments had come from the cuisine she prepared. Her skill at baking was lauded by all of our friends.

It saddened her immensely when she realized she would no longer be able to function in her own kitchen. Her announcement told me more than anything else where her mind was focused and what thoughts preoccupied her.

On another one of our sojourns, after walking together for a half hour or so, Carol squeezed my hand and said, "Vic, my legs feel heavy."

"Are you tired? Should we head home?"

"No, it's my legs. It feels like there are weights tied to my thighs."

It was a sign that her rigidity was progressing. I had already noticed that her tremor had worsened. Whereas it had originally been limited to her left hand, now I could see movement in her forearm, as well as a distinct tremble in her right hand. Still, she was determined that nobody should know. At social functions, she was quick to finish her first drink, because the numbing effects of the alcohol seemed to assuage the tremor. At the dinner table, she took to sitting either with her hands out of sight in her lap, or she would casually cover her left hand with her right to conceal the shaking.

At one Easter dinner, my lovable, if irascible, brother-in-law, who was never known to mince words, caught a glimpse of Carol's briefly unguarded hand. He pointed at it, and in full voice announced, "If I didn't know any better, I'd say you had Parkinson's."

I watched as Carol's face blanched slightly before she quickly recovered and quipped, "Don't be ridiculous, Al," and changed the subject with all the charm and grace she possessed.

My brother-in law's comment may have been impertinent, but it was perceptive. I knew that it was only a matter of time before we would no longer be able to keep the secret. Frankly, I was beginning to be embarrassed by our deception. How long could I, a physician, maintain the charade of a pinched nerve, when lay members of my own family were able to diagnose my wife?

It was shortly after the Easter incident when Carol and I attended another family function. Although the music was in full force, Carol spent the afternoon at a table, chatting happily with everyone and anyone around her. Dancing had been the joy of Carol's life. If there was a band to accommodate her, my wife would dance all night. It didn't matter if it was the foxtrot, the lindy, rock and roll or disco, as long as there was music and a dance partner, she was ecstatic. When I noticed hesitancy in her step and a reluctance to dance to anything with a fast tempo, I knew we had reached a turning point.

I was standing by her when my nephew Ricky came over to say hello. We'd not seen each other in many years, and we hugged and kissed, delighted by the reunion. In his youth, Ricky had been one of the more rebellious of my nephews, but his past also made him one of the most insightful and honest, sometimes to a fault. As Carol turned to join another conversation, Ricky grabbed me by the collar of my jacket and dragged me to the men's room.

"What's with Aunt Carol?" he demanded.

I began the rehearsed story. "It's a pinched nerve in her neck that..."

"Don't bullshit me, Unc!"

I stopped. *He's right*, I thought. *These people all love her and care for her deeply. Sooner or later they will all know. How betrayed will they feel that we lied to them for so long?* So, I took a deep breath and told Ricky the truth. I asked him to keep the information to himself until Carol elected to tell others. He swore he would tell no one.

When we returned home, I broached the subject with Carol. I told her we needed to tell people. I assured her that we could still shield her parents, as they lived two hours away, didn't drive, and were unlikely to be in the company of anyone who would divulge "the secret." Reluctantly, she agreed. Everyone we told—family, our dearest friends, and our son—was devastated by the news.

In time (and faster than we had hoped), Carol's disease progressed beyond the "monitoring" phase and required treatment. Her tremor had worsened still, spreading throughout her extremities. It consumed her every waking moment. She complained of a peculiar feeling in her stomach. She couldn't articulate what it was beyond what it wasn't. It wasn't particularly painful. It wasn't nausea. It wasn't cramps. Her tremor had spread internally, and of all the symptoms she suffered, this was the most discomfiting to her.

We had to find a new neurologist, and hoped we could find one similar to Dr. Doherty—who had since closed his practice and moved out of state—within the network of the nearby university hospital in our community. We were referred to Dr. Philip Morgan, a neurologist who belonged to a large medical group that offered numerous ancillary services.

He started Carol on Artane, a medication designed to alleviate her rigidity and tremor. It had absolutely no effect on her tremor, and we found that the drug caused confusion in Carol. I would come home evenings to find her aimlessly walking about the house, unsure of what she had done that day.

We brought our concerns to Dr. Morgan, who stopped the drug and prescribed Symmetrel. It had little effect. Dr. Morgan tried another medication. And another. None had any merit for Carol. Finally, he started her on a new drug that purported to slow the progression of her disease. (How one could measure such a claim escaped my understanding, but I was not about to challenge his attempt to help my wife.) After two weeks of that therapy, Carol began to experience vivid, terrifying dreams.

"It's like they're in Technicolor," she described to him.

"Yes, that is a common side effect of the drug," Dr. Morgan allowed. "Keep taking it. The dreams won't stop, but I think the benefit is worth it."

"I'm sorry, Doctor, I can't. The dreams are too disturbing. I'll never sleep."

Dr. Morgan gave a heavy sigh and said, "Carol, I'm going to have you see Cathy Nyquist. She's a holistic health practitioner, and member of this medical group. I think she might be a great help to you."

We made an appointment, and as I waited for Carol in the reception area, leafing blindly through a magazine, I wondered what Dr. Morgan thought a holistic health practitioner could hope to offer my wife, when we still hadn't found a medication that provided her any benefit. It's not that I dismiss the healing power of holistic therapy outright, but I must confess that I am a traditionalist at heart. In the absence of scientific, double-blind data, I can only assume that the benefits of alternative medicine come from a psychological component within the patient, and not from actually addressing the presenting disease—in Carol's case, the anatomic lesions in the brain that cause Parkinson's. Then again, it was not my body on the examination table, so if Carol found benefit from it, I was not going to intervene. It had done nothing to assuage my cynicism, however, that the therapist had insisted I pay her in cash.

About a half hour later, Carol emerged from the examination room with a bemused look on her face. She politely said thank you and good-bye. We left the office and headed to the car. We drove home in absolute silence. It was only a two-mile ride, but I felt like we had driven cross-country. After I'd pulled into our driveway and turned off the ignition, I turned to Carol and asked, "So, what is holistic therapy?"

She turned to me with a tear welling in the corner of her eye and said, "She told me to 'embrace' my illness. Can you imagine anyone saying that? She told me to hold my left arm affectionately with my right and tell it that I love it. That I do not hate it." More tears emerged. Carol mimicked Cathy Nyquist's saccharine way of speaking. "'Treat it like an errant child that misbehaved. Pet it. Be kind to it and it will love you in return.'"

With all good intentions I asked, "Did it help?"

"Are you fucking kidding me!?" The tears now flowed in earnest. "They must think I'm some kind of head case if they think that nonsense is going to make me feel better." Carol took a breath and stared forward, trying to compose herself. All of a sudden, she erupted again, "What the hell else does she want me to do with my arm? Put a leash on it and take it for a goddamned walk?" Even in her exasperation, Carol could find a way to make the situation funny. "Honestly, Vic, what kind of neurologist would recommend something like that?"

"What do you want to do?" I asked.

"I'll never go back there," she said, defeated.

"I don't blame you." I leaned across the front seat of the car and pulled her face close to mine. "Listen to me, Carol! You were the supervisor of the chemistry lab in the largest Catholic hospital in America. Don't let some piss-ant destroy your confidence. You know who you are!"

"OK." She got out of the car and gingerly walked unassisted to the front door of our home.

Had anyone in Dr. Morgan's entire medical group spent any substantive time with Carol, they would have quickly learned that my lovely wife came from the mean streets of Hell's Kitchen. Her upbringing, her schooling, and her career nurtured exactness about everything she did. Reasoning with a corporal appendage did not fit that model. Nor did her personal history engender a delicate constitution that wilted with the most minor of discomfort. I believe that, when my wife continued to report unsatisfactory side effects from the medication he prescribed, Dr. Morgan assumed she was a neurotic, and passed her off to a staff member he thought could handle her particular foibles.

Our quest to find a doctor continued. We found a physician nearby who apparently specialized in Parkinson's disease. After Carol filled out endless forms and checklists, we were escorted into Dr. Goldberg's office, where he began to conduct an intake interview. Within minutes, his phone rang. He answered it, spoke for a time, and returned to us. By the time he discerned where he had left off, the phone rang again. This time he apologized before answering, but he proceeded to conduct a long-winded conversation nonetheless. He returned to us and the cycle began again. We chalked it up to one of those chaotic days that befalls any physician in practice. We hoped it had been an anomaly. That was not the case. Every visit with Dr. Goldberg was interrupted by incessant phone calls. The ratio of phone time to patient time was probably nine to one. A bookie spent less time on the phone.

After learning of Carol's history with medication, Dr. Goldberg decided it was time to start her on Sinemet, a standard and time-honored pharmaceutical treatment for Parkinson's disease. Sinemet, like many other drugs, is designed to reduce tremor and relieve rigidity. However, there is a problem that, once a regimen is started, Sinemet generally only has an efficacy from eight to ten years. As such, most neurologists delay its prescription for as long as possible, in lieu of other available treatments. Because Carol was not responding positively to the alternatives, Dr. Goldberg decided there was no more room for delay.

Carol immediately suffered side effects from the drug. Within minutes of ingesting a pill, her entire body would begin to writhe uncontrollably, painfully contorting and twisting itself for hours, until her body naturally eliminated the medication. The benefits she received were trivial at best. Dr. Goldberg tried her on different drugs, new drugs, old drugs, small dosages, large dosages, long-acting versus short-acting versions of the drugs, all with equally unacceptable results. Over the course of a year, Carol tried every single medication on the market.

Ultimately, we came back to Sinemet. It was, after all, the one we knew the most about, it had a proven track record, and Carol found that if she manipulated the dose, she could manage the extent of the side effects. Whereas most patients consumed between four to eight pills daily, Carol could take no more than one, and would portion it for herself by nibbling off little pieces throughout the day. Never could she ingest more than half pill at a time without suffering those horrible extrapyramidal effects.

There is something unusual about Carol's affliction. Classically, a person with Parkinson's exhibits a three-per-second pin-rolling tremor. The hand, for example, rolls from side to side in a fine rhythm that, if timed, moves to and fro precisely three times per second. Carol's tremor was different; the further her disease progressed, the more erratically and wildly her hands and arms would flail about her. While still as rhythmic as a classic Parkinson's patient, Carol's tremor was much more violent. Additionally, a typical Parkinsonian will have difficulty initiating purposeful motion, and once begun, will find it equally difficult to stop. A person trying to walk, for example, might stand in place, frozen and seemingly unable to move. Again, Carol's disability was different. At its worst, she had enormous difficulty with walking. Both of her legs would tremble, wiggling beneath her as though she would scurry away if only her feet weren't glued to the floor. She never had difficulty initiating movement, but it was only with enormous effort that she could manage to control her legs enough to shuffle one foot in front of the other.

Clearly, Carol's case of Parkinson's disease was atypical, and after exhaustive experimentation with different medications, it seemed that her response to standard treatments was atypical as well. Unfortunately, Dr. Goldberg did not see it that way. After a year of unsuccessful results, he had the gall to suggest that the failure of the drugs was a result of Carol's failure to follow his instructions.

When all else fails, by all means, blame the patient.

Needless to say, we said good-bye to Dr. Goldberg, and were once again on the hunt for a neurologist. Carol heard through members of a charity where she volunteered that a new doctor was establishing a practice in the area. He was based at a university hospital in New York, but held office hours one day a week on a college campus ten miles east of us. We made an appointment.

The building at which we were directed to appear turned out to be the campus gymnasium. There was no one to greet us when we entered the makeshift lobby, so we sat in two of the chairs that we assumed had been strewn about to create a waiting area. Several minutes later, Dr. Franklin appeared and led us to his office. It was a pale yellow, cinder block room that probably once served as a broom closet. In the center of the room was a tiny metal desk. Dr. Franklin sat in a tufted swivel chair, and we sat on hard wooden chairs opposite him. A diploma was hung on the wall behind him.

Dr. Franklin asked Carol what was the matter. The word "Parkinson's" had barely escaped her mouth when the doctor took out a yellow legal pad and began to draw the anatomy of the brain. He explained why she needed certain medications to circumvent the anatomic lesion that he drew and circled with his pen. He continued to lecture as he scribbled away, arrows pointing in all directions, chemical names scrawled in the margins, and cross outs indicating abnormal anatomic pathways. I glanced over at Carol, who, bewildered by the exhaustive and unnecessary demonstration before her, looked at me through the corner of her eye and silently mouthed, "What the hell is he doing?!" I shrugged, surmising that the doctor was attempting to demonstrate his profound knowledge of the disease.

When Dr. Franklin finally came up for air, he proposed that Sinemet pills were ultimately of no value, because the absorption of a pill through the stomach was erratic. He prescribed for her a transdermal patch that would deliver the drug at a constant rate. Carol tried it. All it did was provide side effects at a constant rate. Our odyssey continued.

Unable to find an acceptable neurologist locally, I thought it would be worthwhile to venture into Manhattan for consultation with Dr. Shopnick, a world-renowned neurologist based at the highly reputable Neurologic Institute at New York Presbyterian Hospital.

"We have an availability three weeks from Thursday at nine o'clock." The receptionist was not altogether unfriendly when I called for an appointment, but she certainly was all business.

"Whenever! If that's the earliest appointment you have, we'll be happy to take it."

"How would you like to pay for Dr. Shopnick's fee?"

"Well, Carol has Medicare."

"Dr. Shopnick does not accept Medicare. He insists payment be made in full, in advance of the visit. The fee is fully refundable, should you give us thirty-six hours notice of cancellation. Might I suggest a credit card? We accept MasterCard, Visa, Discover and American Express."

Carol had not yet met Dr. Shopnick, let alone spoken to him, and here I was, dutifully reciting my credit card number to a faceless drone on the telephone. There was something unsettling about having to pay up front for a consultation. I'm sure Dr. Shopnick operated this way because the insurance companies would never reimburse his extravagant fee, but it felt unseemly to me for a physician to place monetary interests before a patient's welfare. I was grateful that I had reached a place in life where I could afford it. What would happen to a suffering person who did not have the same financial strength as I?

Three weeks later, we arrived promptly for the appointment, and Carol was immediately presented with another litany of forms to complete. Insurance forms. Personal information forms. Pages indicating next of kin and emergency contacts. Rights of disclosure. Liability releases. And the ubiquitous medical history checklist. *Do you have, or have you ever had any of the following (check all that apply): Heart attack, asthma, blindness, stroke, hearing loss, high blood pressure, elevated cholesterol... Are you on any medication? Do you suffer any allergies?*

It troubles me that a physician thinks he can look at a checklist and assume he has a true grasp of a patient's history.

After we finished with the paperwork, we were ushered into a small cubicle by a resident physician who was so pregnant she looked like she could go into labor at any moment. She asked all the relevant questions and performed a thorough neurologic exam. When she completed it, she spent a considerable amount of time writing her notes in a chart before finally calling Dr. Shopnick to join us. He walked in, sat down and began reading the resident's notes, listening as she related her findings. He didn't so much as look at us. When the resident finished her summary, he declared that Carol was on the wrong medication, and instructed the resident to have a specific member of his staff write a prescription. He laid down the chart and walked out of the cubicle without ever having said a word to either of us.

The medicine was unapproved for use in the United States, so we had to mail the prescription (and a check) to a Canadian address. A package arrived in the mail a few days later. After only one day on the medication, Carol awoke with her stomach tied in knots and her body writhing grotesquely. She was confused, disoriented and frightened. I called the hospital, only to be informed that Dr. Shopnick never accepted phone calls. I requested to speak to the resident physician who had done Carol's intake exam. She had left on maternity leave the day after we saw her. Sensing my mounting frustration, the receptionist assured me that someone would read Carol's chart and get back to us. It took an hour before a doctor we had never met called us with the astute suggestion that Carol stop taking the medication.

We stopped the medication. We also stopped seeing Dr. Shopnick.

Having committed ourselves to the idea of traveling into Manhattan for regular visits to New York Presbyterian, I suggested to Carol that we go see Evelyn Cameron. We both knew Dr. Cameron from her days as a nurse at St. Vincent's. She was an affable woman, who I knew to be very smart, caring and determined. She had graduated the hospital's nursing school and had quickly ascended the ranks to become Head Nurse on the neurology service. After a few years, Evelyn sought further advancement. Nurse Cameron applied to and was accepted at the University of Bologna School of Medicine, and three years later, Doctor Cameron returned to St. Vincent's to begin her residency in the very same neurology department she had left.

Knowing her background (and having been a part of it), I thought Evelyn might be a good match for Carol. She was knowledgeable, yet friendly, she had been a wonderfully caring nurse, and in the intervening years since her return to St. Vincent's, she had established quite a respectable practice.

When we arrived for Carol's appointment, the pleasantries Dr. Cameron exchanged with us were short and perfunctory. She led us to a windowless exam room. It was arranged like any other—a large examination table in the center, a sphygmomanometer and ophthalmoscope on the wall, cabinets, tools, and medical accoutrement—but tucked in the corner was a small desk whose surface was dominated by a large computer. Dr. Cameron sat at the desk and invited Carol to take the chair beside it. I helped Carol to sit, and then retired to the stool in the opposite corner of the room.

Turning away from Carol to face the computer screen, Dr. Cameron began her intake interview.

"So, what brings you here today, Carol?"

As Carol spoke, Dr. Cameron stared intently at the computer monitor, typing furiously like a secretary doing dictation. Even though computerized records were very much in their infancy, the efficiency that they promised had doctors like Evelyn Cameron completely enthralled. At no time during the interview did Dr. Cameron face my wife; she was focused entirely on her computer. When speaking to Carol, she was distant to the point of sounding automated.

"What would you say bothers you most?"

"Right now? It's not even the Parkinson's. It's my back."

"Uh-huh. How long has your back been hurting you?"

"Oh, I've had trouble with it since I was a teenager, but lately..."

"Sorry, hang on a second. I'm not on the right screen here." She clicked through a series of menus, intermittently punching keys on the keyboard, entering data, and searching for the right icon. I marveled at how my colleague had seemingly abandoned the training I knew she had for this infatuation with new technology. A few more clicks with her mouse later, and Dr. Cameron was ready to start typing again. "OK, go ahead."

"What was the question?"

"Your back."

"Ever since I had the horrible dyskinesia from that medication Dr. Shopnick prescribed, I've been getting shooting pains whenever I sit."

"Mm hm." The typing continued. "And what other Parkinson's medications have you tried?"

Carol ran down the laundry list of all the different pills she had taken over the years, and detailed the side effects she suffered from each. Dr. Cameron typed away, entering it all into her computer.

"So, now I'm back to Sinemet, but it's not really helping much."

Dr. Cameron made her final entries, clicked her mouse a few times, then turned around, looked past Carol, and said to me, "Vic, you know the drill. You know the meds. You know what works and what doesn't."

I wanted to scream, "Why the hell are you talking to me? I'm not the patient here! I am the husband, you idiot!"

I suppose it was her idea of professional courtesy, but I found it most discourteous that, if she had nothing relevant to say about the lack of efficacy of Carol's medications, she chose to coldly announce it to me, rather than speak directly to Carol and explain to her that she was at a loss to offer anything else. She stood from her desk and pulled a prescription pad from the drawer.

"I'll tell you, Vic, you are so lucky not to be here anymore," she said as she wrote.

"Why's that?" I asked.

"Practice isn't what it used to be." She tore the top page off the pad.

"Don't I know it."

"Here," Evelyn said, as she handed the paper to me, "Have Carol take one, as needed." It was a prescription for painkillers for her back. In the end, Dr. Cameron had no advice to offer regarding the treatment of Carol's Parkinson's.

Carol and I decided together that the quality of care she would receive from Dr. Cameron was not worth the trek to Manhattan. The hunt continued.

Whereas I was confounded by our inability to find a doctor who had the personality and professionalism that we, or anyone else, should expect, Carol was becoming increasingly depressed by her illness and our inability to treat it. With each passing day, she became more despondent, and it was a rare day for her that she did not cry. I, too, felt a growing sense of helplessness. Nothing I could do mitigated her dread, and there was nothing I could do to mitigate her disease. Days became long and weeks even longer. I poured myself into researching as much as I could about Parkinson's and the newest treatments coming onto the scene.

Ours was a strained existence, one focused merely on getting through the day. It was a far cry from what we had once imagined our lives to be in those early days of marriage, living in Greenwich Village, befriending the local restaurateurs, and meeting at McGowan's or Carmine's after work to laugh with friends over cocktails. How different life had become from those halcyon days when anything seemed possible, and the future was limitless and exciting.

The Neighborhood

Carol and I lived in a one bedroom apartment on the corner of Sixth Avenue and Twelfth Street, two blocks away from the hospital. Greenwich Village was a neighborhood like no other. Citizens of every stripe lived in and around the Village. Congressman Ed Koch, later the three-term Mayor of the City, lived at the foot of Fifth Avenue. Many times I saw Carmine DeSapio, the leader and kingmaker of Tammany Hall who was later convicted of extortion and bribery, walk by my office, wearing his trademark dark brown tinted glasses. Congresswoman Bella Abzug could often be seen around town in an oversized hat large enough to be an umbrella. James Beard, the culinary guru, lived on Twelfth Street directly across from the hospital.

One of the more "colorful" characters who inhabited the Village was Vincent Gigante. He was one of five brothers who grew up on Bleecker Street. One brother was a priest, another had a business, the third was "in the business," and the last was gay. Vinny "The Chin" came to prominence and notoriety when he shot reputed mafia boss Frank Costello as he entered his Upper West Side apartment building. Although ultimately acquitted of the attempted murder charge, Vinny was later convicted of drug trafficking, and spent a number of years in jail. After he was released, my colleague admitted him to St. Vincent's Hospital for observation. On one particular weekend when my colleague was away, it fell to me to care for Chin. He was quite docile when I saw him, but his glare was cold and riveting, and it frightened me. He ground his teeth as he spoke, a habit I found equally disconcerting.

Years later, Vinny the Chin would become the head of the Genovese crime family. He became most well-known for walking the streets of Greenwich Village in a bathrobe and slippers, mumbling and muttering to himself. He was able to avoid prosecution for racketeering for well over seven years, based on his appearance of being *non compos mentis*. It was all a well-orchestrated ruse. He was ultimately exposed, tried and convicted, and the Chin spent his final years in prison.

Living side-by-side with these major public figures were the "regular" denizens. Greenwich Village has a long, storied history of being the epicenter of progressive thinking in New York City. In the early century, it was the center of the bohemian movement. Later, the Village was the home of many speakeasies during Prohibition in the 20s. It was the center for the Beat Generation in the 50s, and was the locus of the anti-war and gay rights movements in the 60s and 70s. All told, the citizenship of Greenwich Village was widely diverse politically, socially, economically and generationally. As such, scores of teenagers and young adults flocked to the Village for its tolerance and the sense of community. They found there others of like mind and spirit. They found a place where they could be themselves. They could socialize. They could find meaningful employment.

A large contingent of these young émigrés was the nation's gays and lesbians. Although there had always been a large gay and lesbian population in the Village, the laws on the books were definitively anti-homosexual. Publicly identifying oneself as gay was an offense worthy of arrest.

My own first encounter with the prejudice of homosexuality occurred while I was a medical officer in the Navy. On one particular morning, I awoke to find that the chaplain on my ship, a man whom I much admired, had been administratively discharged overnight. I learned the reason from the Personnel Officer (an occasional visitor to my beachfront apartment), who had been called to facilitate the paperwork: the chaplain had been caught *en flagrante* on the beach with a seaman. Shore Patrol had arrested him, brought him back to the ship, and the discharge had been affected before the 0700 muster. I learned from the Personnel Officer that any two men caught "in the act" were similarly (always quietly and quickly) discharged from service.

In the early sixties, Mayor Wagner embarked on a campaign to "clean up" the city of its undesirables in anticipation of the New York World's Fair in 1964. Establishments that were known to cater to (or even allow) gay patrons were relentlessly raided, cleared out and closed down by the police. Over the course of the decade, the practice devolved into an elaborate system of bribery and harassment.

It was only three short years after Carol and I had established residence in the Village that perhaps one of the most seminal events in Greenwich

Village history occurred. In 1969 there existed a small bar a few blocks from our apartment called the Stonewall Inn. It catered to the most alienated of gay clientele. Interestingly, it was owned and run by the mafia. On a regular basis (usually early in the evening and with some warning to the proprietors), the police would storm the club, arrest any patron suspected of being a "deviant," and parade them out of the building into the paddy wagon waiting out front. On June 29, 1969, however, the raid came as a surprise late in the evening, and this time (for the first time), the patrons fought back. The confrontation spilled out into Sheridan Square and continued sporadically over the course of several days.

These spontaneous Stonewall Riots forever changed the face of the gay rights movement. Whatever the catalyst, whether it was the tumultuous Vietnam era during which it occurred, or the new, younger generation refusing to abide by the norms of their predecessors, the protestors at Stonewall loudly stated that they refused to live in closets and suffer indignity any longer. Nor would they continue to be passive and quiet.

What I noticed was that among my gay patients and, indeed, some of my colleagues, there was a newfound bounce to their step.

However, be they members of the burgeoning gay rights movement, or the hippies of the anti-war effort, or just America's disenfranchised youth, there was a darker side to the Greenwich Village counterculture. Experimentation—mostly with drugs—ran rampant. The myriad triggers for drug abuse are too many to mention, but people ingested "uppers" and "downers" and injected themselves with intravenous drugs of every kind imaginable. If the Village was the epicenter for drug use and addiction, St. Vincent's Hospital was the refuge for treatment. The number of patients I cared for is countless.

One fellow came into the emergency room feeling ill. Among other superficial complaints, he said he had not urinated in two days. He admitted to smoking marijuana on a regular basis, but he otherwise used no other drugs. His preliminary blood analysis indicated that his kidneys had shut down completely. On further questioning, he revealed that the sensation he got from smoking pot was so gratifying, he reasoned that he could intensify the feeling if he "mainlined" it. He brewed a tea of marijuana leaves and injected himself with it. He certainly got high, but he also sent himself into acute renal failure. Luckily, he was successfully dialyzed and discharged from the hospital with normally functioning kidneys. We wrote up the case and published it in the Journal of the American Medical Association.

While this patient attempted to be resourceful, most addicts simply graduated to stronger drugs.

Next to marijuana, one of the most popular illicit substances of the era was lysergic acid diethylamide (LSD). The hallucinogen was first tested by the CIA as a truth serum. When results of the experimentation were less than successful, the government abandoned the initiative, but the drug made its way to the streets, and "dropping acid" became commonplace. I remember a student from New York University, whose first encounter with drugs was the LSD offered to him by a classmate. After ingesting it, he jumped out of the window of his eighth-floor dormitory room, believing he could fly. Miraculously, he survived the fall, and was brought to the emergency room by ambulance. The X-ray revealed two ends of his fractured spine separated by as much as three inches. When he came down from his high, reality was re-established. He was a permanent paraplegic. It was devastating.

Sexual experimentation was rampant. Along West Street, adjacent to the abandoned piers jutting into the Hudson River, prostitutes of both genders plied their wares. Men solicited men and competed with the ladies of the night. The police were often called to disrupt orgies in the decaying terminals. No longer feeling constrained by society's conservative sexual norms, men began exploring more casual, promiscuous (even anonymous) sexual encounters.

I remember Jerry Bowman, a twenty-two year-old who hailed from a small town in Indiana. He knew he was gay from an early age. He also knew he couldn't survive in his small town, where the teenage pastimes were hunting, fishing, and chasing after girls at the local drive-in. So Jerry came to New York to seek fame and fortune. He gravitated to the fashion industry and found employment at Barney's, which was then a discount clothing store located at Seventh Avenue and Seventeenth Street.

Jerry came to me complaining of a penile drip. Gonorrhea was ruled out by a negative smear and culture. However, a rectal examination revealed an inflamed prostate. Normally, the prostate gland is the size of a walnut and has the consistency of a gum eraser. Jerry's prostate felt like a sac of mashed potatoes. I diagnosed him with non-specific urethritis, and sent him home with a prescription for antibiotics, but not before admonishing him how he should protect himself from infections such as these.

Not a month had passed before Jerry was back in my office, with the same complaint, and the same outcome on rectal examination.

"Jerry, what went wrong?"

"Nothing went wrong, Doctor," Jerry said. "I just fell in love last weekend," he winked.

"Again?"

"Again!"

"Did you at least wear a condom?"

"Doctor K, with all due respect, that's like taking a shower wearing a raincoat."

For years we went through this ritual. Every few months, he'd show up with another drip, we'd try new antibiotics, and I'd counsel him on safe sex. It got to the point that whenever he entered my office, I'd simply ask, "Fall in love again, Jerry?"

"Again!" he'd say, smiling broadly.

I never gave much thought to his lifestyle, other than to note how vastly different it was from mine. Who cared? I was very fond of Jerry. He was truly a nice man, loving, intelligent, well meaning and respectful. To him, the life he was living was worth the occasional inconvenience of a venereal infection. It wasn't until the tsunami of AIDS swept through New York City that the participants really began to question the consequences of such behavior. Sadly, it was too late for Jerry, as his penchant for "falling in love" ultimately led to his demise.

People like Jerry made the Village a special place to live, a melting pot within the melting pot called New York. I remember most vividly patients like him, those people who'd likely be labeled as eccentric. To me they were the salt of the earth. They energized my life, and in my opinion, added much to the fabric of the society in which we lived.

Mary Mallon was a wealthy widow who would arrive at my office in a chauffeured limousine. She was almost totally incapacitated from arthritis. When I first asked her to lay down on my examining table, she looked at me with the sternness of a nun and said, "Chickens lay eggs. People lie down." Despite my grammatical gaffe, Mrs. Mallon remained my patient for years, and when my son was born, she beamed as she handed me a beautifully embroidered wool baby's blanket wrapped in the most exquisite paper and tied with an elaborate ribbon. She wished me and my wife years of happiness. I was touched beyond words by her gesture.

Giacomo Marchesi lived in a walk-up tenement apartment on Kenmare Street, a few blocks away from the famous Eileen's Cheesecake. He suffered with ascites, an abnormal accumulation of fluid in his abdomen due to end-stage liver disease. (We thought it was due to alcoholism, but in retrospect, with what we know now, he probably had Hepatitis C.) There was no specific treatment for his condition beyond supportive care. He was profoundly uncomfortable, weak, and in full knowledge that his days on earth were numbered. The long walk to my office was agony, but there was not one office visit that Giacomo did not bring with him a cheesecake from Eileen's. No matter how often I told him that he need not spend his money on such a luxury for me, he replied that it was his pleasure to do so.

Yuletide, especially, was a season of extravagant riches. Every Christmas, patients presented me with various tokens of appreciation: bottles of liquor, clocks, sterling silver tie tacks, cuff links from Christian Dior. I've collected perhaps thirty silver or gold pen and pencil sets, many from Cross, more from Tiffany & Co. Such warmth, generosity, and gratitude from so many people made being their physician so much more to me than just a job. My patients felt like family.

After eight years of working together, Maureen and I parted ways. I was sad to see her go, because she left big shoes to fill. It didn't take long for word to spread around the St. Vincent's community that I was looking for a replacement. The supervisor of the records department came to my office and begged me to consider her daughter, Rose, who worked as an aide in the Reiss Psychiatric Pavilion. I agreed to an interview. It took less than ten minutes for me to realize I had to hire her.

Rose grew up in the Village. She came from a large extended family, many of whom had history with St. Vincent's. Like Maureen, she was brilliant at reading people and understanding their moods (mine, perhaps most importantly, included). Whereas Maureen related to people intuitively, I'm sure Rose's skill came from her experience working in Reiss. She had more insight into people than most shrinks I knew. Often were the times I would ask her for her opinion about a patient whose mental state lay outside what I thought was the framework of normalcy. Rose's assessments were always intuitive, sharp and reasoned. She was able to relate so well with my patients, many of whom spent as much time with her as they did with me.

One day Rose came into my office with a bemused smirk on her face. She had just taken preliminary information from a new patient.

"Wait till you get a look at this one," she said, gesticulating with her thumb.

"What's wrong?" I replied.

"You'll see," she said as she walked out, chuckling down the hall.

Working in close quarters with one person all day, there inevitably was an occasional inclination to gossip about patients. It lightened the day, and the exchanges never extended beyond the front door of the office. In all the years of my practice, I had but two secretaries. Both could pass the most stringent CIA test for security. Never once did either betray a confidence, but that does not mean that we didn't make each other giggle from time to time.

Ethel Sachs walked in to my consultation room. Aged 75, this wrinkled old lady had a head of impeccably coifed, flaming red hair. The red tresses transformed her into a typical New York curiosity, one who looked so much younger than she actually was. In reality, it was a wig she wore to cover her close-cropped, thinning, gray hair. The impression of her with and without the wig was stunning. I gave her a lot of credit for her fortitude (translation: chutzpah).

Ethel's medical problems were as serious as her demeanor was light-hearted. She had severe uncompromising angina pectoris. Her coronary artery disease was so advanced that virtually any activity provoked crushing chest pain that riveted her in her tracks. She was well aware of her mortality, and had seen a number of physicians, but could not establish a relationship with any of them. It was no wonder to me, because Ethel was, as they say in Yiddish, a *yenta*, a garrulous, talkative gossip. She talked nonstop about everything and nothing at all. She didn't know how to stop. She spoke incessantly, fearing, I suppose, that if she stopped, she would somehow cease to live.

Other physicians quickly got irritated with Ethel, and managed to exclude her from their practice. That didn't seem necessary to me. I found that all I had to do was to listen to the limit of my tolerance, and then merely announce that the office visit was over. Ethel would mechanically get up, walk over to Rose's desk and steal her ear. Happily, Rose's tolerance was greater than mine.

The treatment for Ethel was two parts listening and one part pill. She had trials of nitroglycerin, long-acting nitrates, and beta blockers, all with varying success. Cardiac surgery was still in its infancy, and at her age, was probably not a viable option, anyway. Venting her fears was important to her, and she soon began to convey concern about her husband, who had high blood pressure but never took care of it; she was afraid that he would die one day and leave her all alone. She asked me if I would examine and treat him. Of course, I answered affirmatively.

It was a full year before Julius Sachs appeared in my office. He was a suspicious man by nature, although very pleasant. He was, in fact, jocular. During the first visit, we spent most of the time exchanging banter, just getting to know one another. Whenever I diverted the conversation to medicine, he retreated into another joke or wisecrack. Eventually he allowed me to get to the reason for his visit. I took a medical history and led him to the examining room.

Julius had been hypertensive for many years and had treated his condition with benign neglect. Now, his blood pressure was at an alarming 240/130. His heart was enlarged, which was no surprise, and he had a bruit in his neck (a rumbling sound indicative of a narrowed artery). His electrocardiogram reinforced what I had found. I would have liked to put Julius in the hospital, to investigate the bruit and address his extreme blood pressure. But, knowing that it took Ethel over a year of cajoling just to get Julius to come and see me, I wasn't about to lose my rapport with him before it was even established.

Instead, we discussed his disease for a while and I explained the need for therapy. I wasn't about to embark on a crash program. Inasmuch as he had lived with hypertension for so many years, it would have been imprudent to rapidly correct his pressure. I outlined to him a plan to prescribe a less-than-normal dose of antihypertensive medicine, and gradually increase the quantity until his pressure was controlled. He seemed comfortable with the plan. It smacked of being reasonable. It certainly did not appear to be impetuous.

He returned several weeks later, and I adjusted the dose of his medication. We discussed the bruit in his neck. I drew a few diagrams to explain what it was, and I suggested a few diagnostic tests I was considering. He dismissed them all out of hand. Still, he agreed to return again in a month's time.

He did not show up for his next appointment. Calls to him and Ethel went unanswered.

The news came by phone. A neighbor of theirs called to ask if I heard about Mr. and Mrs. Sachs. It seemed that Julius had some kind of seizure and collapsed to the floor. (He undoubtedly had a stroke as a result of the narrowed artery in his neck.) Ethel, in a state of panic and hysteria, neglected to call 911, and instead attempted CPR. As she was giving Julius mouth-to-mouth resuscitation, she was seized with chest pain and collapsed. As neighbors rushed from their apartments to assist her, she was able to relate only part of the story. She died before the ambulance arrived. He was already dead.

I am often struck by who I remember from my life as a physician. Over the course of twenty years, the number of patients one may care for is countless. Add to that the interrelationships with patients' family members and friends, and after a few short years, it becomes almost impossible to recall any one at random. Patients who predictably get well are the first to be forgotten, which is hardly fair, considering they are the ones who provide motivation to go to work each morning. It's those who fail therapy, or the ones I feel I somehow failed as a doctor that I find haunting.

A longstanding patient of mine who lived in the Chelsea section of New York referred the Rosenbaums to me. Among other things, Chelsea was a residential community for retired garment workers. Having a casual acquaintance with the garment industry, I knew that the Rosenbaums lived on a meager retirement income, so I accepted them as patients for whatever their insurance provided.

Hyman was eighty-four years old and had heart failure. After several heart attacks, the remaining functional muscle in his heart barely supported his circulation. He was taking an array of medicines prescribed by a number of different doctors, and he became confused by the complexity of his medication schedule. There was not much I could do for his heart failure except to ensure that he took his medicine properly and on time. To help ease the confusion, I sorted the pills that were essential into one schedule, and listed the less critical medicine on a separate schedule.

Hyman was a sweet old man who loved life. He was embarrassed by his invalidism. He wanted to go to the movies. He wanted to be able to dance, but he barely had enough energy to walk a few steps, let alone do a foxtrot. Above all, Hyman wanted to eat. Unfortunately, whenever he dined in a local cafeteria or diner, he would inevitably wind up in the emergency room later that night in acute pulmonary edema, literally drowning in fluids that his heart could no longer pump out of his lungs, undoubtedly caused by the high salt content of the commercial food. Sometimes he would be treated with diuretics and sent home. Other times he required two or three days in the hospital to stabilize his failing heart.

Sophie, by contrast, was a tiny dynamo. She was crowding eighty, but wouldn't admit it. I was treating her for emphysema, but I knew that she still sneaked a cigarette now and again when Hyman was napping. She would wander out into the hallway of her apartment and puff away until the coughing consumed her, then return to the afternoon soap operas on television. She confessed all of this to me one day in a moment of weakness, but I found it impossible to reprimand her. At her age, after a lifetime of smoking, it hardly mattered that she indulged herself with a couple of cigarettes every day.

These two charming, delightful people were in love. It was obvious. They held hands affectionately, like teenagers. She would lean across the couch in the waiting room and give him a kiss on the cheek just to fluster him. Hyman would often say to me "Fix me up good, Doc, Sophie's been waiting a long time for me to take her to bed." Sophie would giggle, and whisper to me, "Oh, if anything ever happened to my Hymie, I'd kill myself."

Over the next two years, all the times I saw Sophie, she would mention how empty her life would be without Hyman. Just as often, I took a few moments to impress upon her the reality that she needed to accept the fact that her husband was approaching the end of his life. It's easy to be philosophical about life when it's not your own, but I thought that my gentle reminders of Hyman's mortality would be helpful so that she could prepare to make a life for herself when he was gone.

The inevitable came. One day, Hyman slipped into profound, unremitting heart failure that no longer responded to medication. I admitted him to the hospital and provided as much comfort as humanly possible. Hyman needed a new heart, but it was not a consideration at his age (nor was the technology available at the time). He lapsed into a deep sleep from which he could not be awakened. Throughout, Sophie sat vigil by his bedside, arriving early in the morning and leaving only to go home to sleep. A week later, Hyman died peacefully with his loving wife holding his hand. Sophie took the news surprisingly well, which reassured me that the advice I had been giving her had, in fact, helped. When I extended my heartfelt condolence, she kissed me.

"I know you did everything that could be done for my Hymie, Doctor. Thank you," she whispered. "He liked you so much, and it meant everything to him to have a doctor that he respected."

I flushed with pride, and was deeply embarrassed to receive that kind of adulation at such a somber moment. She was so much older than I that her remarks reminded me of how I felt when I was a child and my grandmother praised me.

"You come and see me any time, Sophie, OK?"

"I'll call next week. After I sit shiva."

One week later, Rose—my secretary, bookkeeper, confidante, and trusted friend—burst into my consultation room, weeping. She had just gotten off the phone. Someone called to inform us that Sophie had thrown herself from the roof of her six-floor apartment complex and died.

Nothing will ever erase the memory of that telephone call. To this day, I wonder how much more credence I should have given to her idle comments about not being able to live without Hyman. I sleep better believing it would have made no difference, but sleep is not always sound. I sleep because of fatigue, but still I dream. And think. Thoughts rumble through like freight trains, or creep in like cat burglars. Thoughts that shriek like sirens in the night: what I might have done, what I should have done, what I failed to do. Sometimes the thoughts are reassuring: that I did my best, that there is nothing more I could have done. But the thoughts still echo, nevertheless.

A Curious Case of Coma

An operator on the public address system was announcing my name repeatedly, urgently advising me to call an extension in the Reiss Pavilion. Much to my surprise, instead of a nurse or ward clerk, Charlie Ratigan answered the phone, and his voice was distressed and uneasy.

"I need your help!"

"What's the matter, Charlie? You sound tense."

"Can you answer a consult right away?"

"Of course. What's the problem?"

"Come over to Reiss 3 and I'll tell you."

"I'll be there in five minutes."

I had just finished entering a note into the progress page of a chart and written a few orders to expedite the care of my patient, so I went to track down the nurse on duty. I found her puffing on a cigarette in the ladies' room. It was not unusual to walk in unannounced because it was more often used for cigarette breaks than as a bathroom. Besides, the commode was tucked behind a partition that provided privacy. I showed my written orders to the nurse and read them aloud. I had deluded myself into thinking that this compulsive act would ensure their accurate and prompt implementation.

The nurse, seated on a three-legged wooden stool with her legs crossed, absently nodded through a cloud of smoke. Her elbow rested on her knee, her chin was cradled in the palm of her hand, and she held her cigarette an inch from her mouth. Her hair lay on her head like a damp mop. She neither looked up at me nor at the orders I held in front of her. After replacing the chart in its rack and flagging it with a clothes pin, I walked down the corridor to the elevator and pushed the button. It was three o'clock in the afternoon and I knew—as surely as I knew the elevator would soon appear—

that my orders would not be picked up. With one hour to a change in shift, no one would even look at the chart. The only question that remained was when would the incoming group page me? The odds were favorable that it would be during dinner time.

The Reiss Pavilion was the building at St. Vincent's Hospital dedicated to psychiatric service. The short walk along Twelfth Street refreshed me. Spring was in full bloom in New York. Luxuriant green ivy covered the facades of the brownstones up and down the street. It shimmered in the cool breeze. Lush wisteria vines curled up wrought iron fences, their purple flowers adding an intoxicating layer of fragrance to the air. This was the concrete jungle's answer to spring in suburbia. Limited as it may have been, the tapestry was a welcome sight and was infinitely better than the muddy snow and dirty slush of winter.

Stepping out of the elevator on the third floor of Reiss, I pressed the buzzer beside the door to the locked unit. Looking through its small glass window, I waited, frustrated, until the nurse ambled ever so slowly down the corridor to unlock the door and admit me to the unit. At the same glacial pace, she led be back to her station before notifying Dr. Ratigan of my arrival.

Dr. Charlie Ratigan was not a typical psychiatrist. In my experience, most psychiatrists seemed to have known their career path since high school, and suffered through college and medical school simply so they could reach their goal. For them, internship was a total bore. The thought of having to take care of people with pneumonia or sepsis was antithetical to their pursuit to understand the inner workings of the mind. Charlie was cut from a different bolt of fabric. He was the most promising surgical resident to have graced St. Vincent's Hospital in a decade. He was a member of Alpha Omega Alpha, the most prestigious academic honorary society in medical school. He was Irish. He was Catholic. He was from Yale. He was God's gift to surgery.

The day on which he announced his intention to abandon surgery and enter psychiatry was akin to the day King Edward abdicated his throne, the day President Johnson declined a second term, the day Nixon resigned the presidency...all rolled into one.

Charlie and I interned together, and although our residency training was interrupted by our respective military service, we were now both in private practice. I admired him. He was a sensitive psychiatrist who did not place much stock in Freudian psychobabble, nor did he confound colleagues and patients with psychiatric jargon. Neither did he pray at the altar of traditional psychoanalytical hyperbole. Charlie had an uncommon insight into people's emotions. He seemed to know intuitively the dynamics of interpersonal relationships. He had that sense of knowing when to probe and when to listen. He always maintained a professional and appropriate distance, but still seemed to assume the role of older brother. He was a good doctor.

He trusted me, I suppose, because I never let him down. I told him what I knew, and if I didn't have a medical answer for a patient's complex problem—often a mystery beyond my comprehension—I wasn't afraid to tell him so. After my consultation with one of his patients, he was secure in knowing that he was dealing with a psychological disorder rather than a medical problem hiding behind symptoms of a psychiatric nature.

Bounding down the corridor, Charlie's haste indicated more than concern. His expression was one of sheer panic. The patient he wanted me to see on this day was a total enigma. One does not lapse into coma in a hospital, in a locked psychiatric ward, without good reason.

"Let's get a cup of coffee," I said, and led Charlie to the dining room. "Tell me the story from the beginning and we'll try to piece it together."

He proceeded to tell me that his patient was referred to him several weeks previously. She had recently entered into a homosexual liaison and was experiencing a great deal of remorse. A Catholic, her feelings of guilt bordered on a reactive depression whose root, Charlie surmised, was deepseated and probably surfaced intermittently. She "acted out" by exhibiting hostile and aggressive behavior, and Charlie wasn't certain if she was suicidal. Knowing that removing a patient from his or her everyday environment and its attendant stressors can sometimes be therapeutic in and of itself, Charlie suggested she enter the hospital to be thoroughly evaluated. She was quite reluctant to admit herself to the psychiatric unit. It took a hard sell because Jean Richard was a nun.

Sister Jean had arrived at the hospital that morning dressed in street clothes so as to mitigate the embarrassment she might experience had she worn her habit. She was processed in the usual manner. She had entered the hospital through the admitting office, had her insurance verified, and had signed a mountain of forms and disclaimers. She was escorted to the third floor of Reiss. While awaiting the intern who would take her medical history and perform a thorough physical examination, the floor nurse helped Sister Jean change into a hospital gown. The nurse packed away the patient's clothes, which were then sent to the basement for storage. (Patients in the Reiss Pavilion were not permitted to keep personal items, because hairbrushes, toothbrushes, and such were viewed as potential weapons or instruments of self-harm. In the case of the mentally ill, such precautions are taken in all reputable institutions.) Once Sister Jean was settled in, the floor nurse suggested that she take a nap until the intern arrived to examine her. The patient obliged by puffing up her pillow and drawing up a thin blanket.

When the intern arrived, he entered the room and announced himself. He was greeted with silence. Such behavior was not unusual in the psychiatric ward. Sometimes a patient's attitude is one of passive indifference, other times it manifests as downright hostility. The young doctor advanced to the bed and saw that the patient was lying on her side, facing the wall. When she continued to ignore him, he approached her and announced that he would assist her in turning over. As he rolled her to a supine position on the bed, her arm flopped down on the mattress with such weight that he realized he was dealing with more than a sleeping patient. Unable to rouse her, the intern became alarmed and notified the head nurse. All at once, the unit was abuzz with activity.

Nurses, doctors, orderlies, and even a representative from administration were present at the conclave outside Sister Jean's room. Nobody could explain how a patient—a nun, at that—could walk into the hospital, enter a locked floor, be supervised as she undressed, and then slip into a coma within two hours of her arrival.

Beads of perspiration dotted Charlie's forehead as he concluded his recitation of the patent's history. His coffee cup contained only dregs. He took a long puff on his cigarette and, looking directly at me, said, "My ass is in a wringer. Administration is crawling up my back; first, for admitting a lesbian nun, and now demanding answers as to how and why she went into a coma."

"I'm not clairvoyant, Charlie, so let me start by examining her. She didn't have access to pills or needles, did she?"

Charlie looked at me irritably. "How the hell could she get pills on a locked ward?"

"Charlie," I said, "don't get crazy with me. If you don't ask the question, you don't get an answer." I tried to lighten his anxiety. "You shrinks only listen. We internists live and die by questions." I stood up and walked to the door. "Give me a few minutes to examine her and we'll talk again."

The patient lay motionless on the bed. Her blood pressure, pulse, and temperature were normal. Her pupils were midsize and reacted to the light of my flashlight. She did not, however, react to my attempt to elicit pain by squeezing her Achilles' tendon. No reflexes were present; not a knee jerk, not a biceps, nothing. A plantar reflex in her foot was not elicited. Her neck was supple. She was in Stage 3 coma and no one knew why, least of all me. I was listening to her heart when Charlie walked in and took a position on the other side of the patient's bed.

"Any clues?"

"No," I responded, "But I'll tell you what it's not. It's not meningitis or a stroke. She looks like an overdose of sleeping pills, but you tell me she had no access to any."

"That's correct," he said.

"Well, along with the usual blood work, I think we should do a TLC."

"What have I missed during my two years in the Air Force?"

"It's not tender loving care, Charlie," I said.

"What is a TLC?"

"Thin-layer chromatography. It's new and we're able to do it now in our lab."

"But it's four-thirty in the afternoon!"

"I know," I said, "but I have influence. Have you forgotten? I married the supervisor of the chemistry lab."

He laughed, greatly reducing the almost palpable tension in the room. Charlie knew Carol from our days on the house staff. He recalled how I met her by accident when I literally bumped into her in a corridor during my year as Chief Resident, how our courtship was a whirlwind, and how quickly we decided to marry.

"Will she stay late to do the test?"

"Of course she will! Don't you remember Dr. Vitale's daughter?"

The girl had been born prematurely with a blood type incompatibility, and Carol stayed up all night doing sequential bilirubin assays while the pediatricians debated whether or not to do an exchange transfusion.

"You know, Charlie, no one asked her to do it. She volunteered."

The head nurse walked in, and I asked her to rush a sample of urine and a vial of blood to the chemistry lab. I picked up the telephone to tell my wife that dinner would be late for both of us...again.

It was early evening when I was paged. I knew the telephone extension before the page operator could say it aloud. It was the lab.

"Carol?"

"I have your results, O Great Wizard," she said, the smile on her face clearly evident in the tone of her voice.

"Thank you for your professionalism, dear. What's the good news?"

"The good news isn't so good. Not only will you not get your dinner, you will not get anything else tonight either."

"Why?" I asked.

"Your patient has both glutethimide and a barbiturate in her urine."

"That's impossible," I said. "She's on a locked ward in Reiss."

I could hear the smile fading from the voice on the other end of the phone.

"You had me stay three hours late to do this damn test so you could argue the results with me?" Her tone was low and threatening.

"No, no! I'm not arguing with you. I'm just troubled. The patient is in a coma, administration is in an uproar, Charlie Ratigan is on a hot seat, and I'm now involved, too. Will you do one more favor for me?"

There was silence at the other end. She knew what I was going to ask.

"Will you do the barbiturate blood level?"

"Are you crazy?" The smile in Carol's voice was gone. "That test is a beast!"

"But this lady is in a coma. Please."

"Why did I marry a doctor? You're behaving like a resident again. If I had married Tony, I could be having dinner at El Morocco right now."

"I love you, Carol," I trilled, my voice sweet as honey. I felt a little guilty, because her job demanded that she be on her feet all day. Carol often complained of backache, and now she would have to spend several more hours before she could relieve the strain.

"You're a pain in the ass."

"I know, but please hurry."

Our conversations were often marked by mock annoyance, but Carol always sensed when I was concerned and needed immediate results. She obliged me because I rarely abused the laboratory's time, but I wondered where I would be had I not been able to get the results I wanted when I most needed them. Where would the patients be? Was successful medicine predicated on who could barter the most influence?

After a few moments of pondering these questions, I turned my attention to the immediate problem I faced. The finding of glutethimide, a sedative prescribed under the brand name Doriden (now rarely, if ever, prescribed for the treatment of insomnia in the United States), was worrisome. That, consumed with an unknown quantity of a barbiturate, could well be the reason that Sister Jean was now comatose.

I was lost in these thoughts when Sister Ruth, the hospital administrator, walked into the lounge and whispered my name. I stood up, startled.

"Excuse me Sister, I must have dozed off. I'm waiting for the results of some blood tests."

"Oh, no! Pardon me, Doctor, I didn't mean to startle you."

We both sat down and exchanged pleasantries. She began by reminding me how pleased the administration had been with my performances as a resident physician. She expressed her interest in my budding career and her pleasure that I had married the supervisor of the chemistry lab. St. Vincent's employees became surrogate family to Sister Ruth, and she could not be happier when nurses or lab technicians fell in love with young doctors and married them. But this evening's conversation contained an undercurrent. Her tone and tenor changed perceptibly when we began to discuss the status of Sister Jean Richard.

"You know, Doctor, it would be a terrible embarrassment to the religious community if Sister Jean Richard's sexual proclivities were known."

I replied that I emphatically agreed. Actually, I was so taken aback by the directness of her comment that I had no alternative but to agree. I quickly realized, however, that Charlie Ratigan had related this information to me verbally and in confidence. I had not yet written my consultation report. (Not that I ever would have written in the record anything referable to her sexuality. I was an internist called to determine the cause of her coma. Her private life was of no concern.) The intern had arrived only after the patient lapsed into a coma. He could not have learned of Sister Jean's sexual orientation. So how had Sister Ruth come upon such sensitive information? How many people in administration already knew that Sister Jean was a lesbian?

When I confronted her with this question, Sister Ruth bristled. She stood up and took a deep breath. As she exhaled, she said, "You have a promising career, Doctor, but you need to know that St. Vincent's is a family. While at times we are privy to certain information about a patient, there are confidences we need to keep private."

"Why would the Sisters of Charity at St. Vincent's be embarrassed by the sexual preference of a nun from another community?" She simply stared at me. "Are you suggesting," I stammered, "that I modify my written report to save the religious community any embarrassment?"

"I'm suggesting nothing. I am merely making a statement that we are a family here. You may interpret that statement as you wish."

She spun and walked toward the door. Without facing me directly, she remarked rather cryptically, "Doctors come and go, but the religious community is here forever." With that, she sailed out the door, her habit fluttering behind her.

My mouth was agape. Time stood still as I contemplated her remarks, watching the shadow of the woman framed in the frosted glass of the door.

While I waited for Carol to call with the lab results, I went back to Sister Jean's room and examined her again from head to toe, finding no new clues. I called to the nurse to fetch me a glove so I could do a pelvic examination. She glared at me with utter disbelief, even contempt, clearly written on her face.

"You're going to do a pelvic exam on a nun?" she hissed.

"Do you live in the fifteenth century?" I barked back.

I was by then a bit irritable. It had already been a long day. I certainly wasn't about to explain to the floor nurse what a complete examination entails. I had no interest in learning about her prejudices, her perception of the clergy, or if my exam would become gossip that spread so fast as to make the public address system redundant.

I snapped on a glove and reminded the nurse to remain in the room. There was never an excuse for examining a woman without a witness in attendance. The unconscious state of this patient did not abrogate her right to this long-standing practice. It was a good thing that I had demanded the nurse's attendance because my fingers had no sooner entered the patient's vagina than they encountered a firm round resistance. My face must have mirrored my surprise.

"Did you find a tampon, Doctor?" the nurse asked with the crispness of a stale cracker.

I probed a little further and discovered that the object in her vagina was cylindrical. As I extracted it and held it up, the nurse's face changed from frank irritation to abject pity. What I held in my hand was an empty plastic medicine vial.

"How miserable do you have to be," I whispered, "to try and commit suicide in the psychiatric unit of a hospital?"

My nameless nurse looked at me, and with a particular arrogance announced, "People cry out in different ways."

I am sure she thought she had said something profound, but I chose to regard her comment as rhetorical.

Just then, the phone rang. When I picked up the receiver, Carol's exhaustion was readily apparent.

"Your patient is in big trouble!"

"Is there any good news?" I asked.

"Her barbiturate level is ten milligrams per cent."

It was a stunning number, considering it should have been zero.

"Is it a short-acting or long-acting barbiturate?" I asked.

"I don't know," she said. "Our qualitative test is not specific. When do you think you'll be home?"

"I don't know. Those numbers dictate that we do something drastic. I'll grab a sandwich. Don't wait up."

"What do you mean, 'drastic?'" she asked.

"Well, if it were only a barbiturate, we could flush out most of it through her kidneys by giving her an osmotic diuretic, but because she also took Doriden, we're up the creek without the proverbial paddle."

"What are you going to do?"

"I'll probably have to dialyze her."

"See you tomorrow," she said with knowing finality. "I'm going to have a gin and tonic and get off my feet."

Dialysis, under the best circumstances, was a five-hour procedure. But because the patient had not yet been transferred to the dialysis unit from the Reiss Pavilion, it would likely be an eight-hour marathon.

I paged Dr. Ratigan. Charlie was speechless when I related my findings to him in the hallway. Our conversation was really more of a monologue; I spoke, he listened. I outlined a plan of action and suggested that he transfer Sister Jean's care to me until she became conscious and was deemed medically stable. It was really a formality and a technicality, as psychiatrists could not attend patients in the intensive care unit or the general hospital under their own supervision, but rather could only admit them to and attend them in the Reiss Pavilion.

Just then, a nurse bolted from Sister Jean Richard's room.

"Oh, Doctor, I was just about to page you. Sister's blood pressure fell to ninety over sixty."

"Transfer her immediately to the intensive care unit," I ordered, "and notify them that I want to start peritoneal dialysis as soon as she reaches the floor."

Barbiturates are readily dialyzable. Doriden is not. Doriden binds to the fats in the body and cannot be easily filtered out through the cellophane membrane of the dialysis coil. When a patient ingests more than one hypnotic drug, the results might only be additive; however, in some cases, they may be synergistic, so the effect is greater than it would be if each drug were taken independently. In other words, each drug magnifies the effects of the other. I had to remove as much of one drug as I could, and then allow her body's metabolism to take care of the remainder.

I had planned on hemodialysis, which would have cleansed Sister's blood of barbiturates more efficiently. However, hemodialysis requires tapping an artery to bring blood to the dialysis coil. Now that her blood pressure was falling, that option was out. My only hope—and, really, her only hope— was that peritoneal dialysis would be successful. In peritoneal dialysis, the lining of the abdomen, the peritoneum, serves the same function as the external hemodialysis coil. The process does not, however, rely on blood pressure, and although less efficient, it is equally as effective.

There was no time to waste. Soon her pulmonary system would be in jeopardy. If her lungs failed to function, death was inevitable.

As soon as Sister Jean was transferred to her ICU bed, I dressed her abdomen with an antiseptic and inserted a trochar into her belly. I inserted a catheter through the metal tube, removed the trochar, and connected the first two-liter bottle of dialysis fluid to the catheter. After instructing the house staff, the resident physician, and the intern on duty how to manage the patient, I headed home for what remained of the night.

Carol and I lived within walking distance from the hospital and, having had no dinner and feeling exhausted, I rationalized that I was completely justified in leaving at one o'clock in the morning. I had, after all, been on the go since six-thirty that morning. I crawled into bed and fell fast asleep before my head hit the pillow.

Morning arrived too soon. I was jarred awake by the alarm clock. Showering, shaving, and drinking a quick cup of coffee constituted a well-orchestrated ritual lasting but a half hour. I left as Carol was munching on an English muffin topped with sautéed mushrooms and bacon. I would have liked to have had a large breakfast with her, but my weight in the first few years of marriage had soared from one hundred fifty pounds when I was in the Navy to over one hundred sixty five pounds. I was beginning to look like a pear. I ordinarily found excuses to leave the apartment before breakfast, but on that day I didn't need one.

I walked into the ICU at five past seven to learn that not only did Sister Jean's blood pressure stabilize but also that her knee-jerk reflex reappeared. Moreover, her urine output was a brisk two milliliters per minute after dialysis was terminated. Her prospect for recovery was excellent.

As I left her room, a familiar rush of excitement overcame me: the thrill of success, and the joy of knowing I did something worthwhile for someone else. I had not yet exchanged a single word with the patient, and I was feeling very good about myself. I had no sooner completed my optimistic note in the medical record and rewritten new orders for the day when my beeper sounded. I called my answering service to learn that I was paged to call an extension unfamiliar to me.

I dialed the number and found myself conversing with Mr. Hadden in the business office. He introduced himself and segued into a series of banal statements: he knew I was taking care of Sister Jean Richard, he knew she was ill, he knew that I was working diligently to save her life.

"Mr. Hadden," I interrupted, "it's going to be a long day. What are you trying to tell me?"

"Well, it has to do with Sister's insurance."

"What about it?" I asked.

"Her insurance doesn't cover this illness."

"I'm accustomed to taking care of the clergy without charging a fee, Mr. Hadden, if that's what you are alluding to?"

"That's only part of it, Doctor," he stated, sounding very much like the bean counter he was. "She has hospital insurance, but her current problem isn't covered. You see, it's a technicality. She was admitted to the psychiatric unit with a diagnosis of depression, which would have been covered by her insurance, but she attempted suicide and that is excluded in her policy. Therefore, any complications from the suicide attempt, including what you're doing in the ICU, are not covered. I don't have to tell you how much everything costs in the ICU."

"How do you know she attempted suicide? Was it on Channel 2 News this morning?" I was incredulous. "I can't understand how such private and sensitive information is bandied about so that even someone in the business office knows about it before I've even had a piece of toast!"

Mr. Hadden pleaded with me not to get excited. He wanted me to understand the hospital's position in monetary matters. There were funds set aside for the care of the clergy and certain perks were offered to them. But he was anxious to have me understand that the way a hospital chart was worded could make the difference between automatic payment and rejection by an insurance carrier. He droned on, and I murmured an occasional "uh huh," only half-listening to anything he said.

With Mr. Hadden's words echoing in my head, we transferred Sister Jean back to the Reiss Pavilion later that very afternoon. By the end of the day, she had regained all of her senses. She recovered from the overdose, and she returned to Dr. Ratigan's care.

Still, I visited her as often as I could on my way to my office. It was merely a courtesy. On the first day, we introduced ourselves to each other as if the previous two had never happened. We spoke at length about familiar things: about growing up in Brooklyn, about being raised in a large family. We specifically danced around anything having to do with what she had done. Somehow in those brief encounters and conversations, we bonded. There is no way to explain how some relationships are instant and others require months to years to develop, if ever they do.

It was toward the end of office hours many days later that I received a telephone call from the head nurse on Reiss 3. Apparently, Sister Jean had abdominal pain and would let none of the house staff examine her. Would I come back to the hospital to see her?

I assured her I would as soon as my last patient was seen at about seven o'clock. In the meantime, not knowing the degree or location of her pain, I instructed her not to feed the patient her dinner. When I arrived on the floor, Sister Jean was alert, irritable, cranky, and cross.

"I didn't expect you to treat me like all the others," she said as I entered her room.

"What do you mean?" I replied.

"Just because I'm disfigured is no reason to ignore me."

Her outburst could not have been more shocking than if she had slapped me on the face. It was her harelip. In the excitement and frenzy of the first night and ensuing hectic days of recovery, I had made a mental note of her harelip, but disregarded its significance, as it had nothing to do with the clinical problem at hand.

My sister had suffered with both scoliosis and poliomyelitis. She was left with an unmistakable hump on her back. I never took notice of it as a child. It was merely part of her anatomy. One day a friend asked me about it. His question took me aback. I never thought of it as something that would draw others' attention. I knew it was there, and I knew why it was there, but I had never seen it as an abnormality. Nor did I realize what lasting effect it might have had on her. With Sister Jean, while the physical abnormality of her harelip was unimportant to dealing with her coma, I likewise neglected to account for the emotional impact it had on the patient.

There is an aphorism we learned as part of Dr. Jaegers's curriculum in medical school that served me well as a practicing physician: "If you listen to your patients, they will tell you what is the matter."

"Are you embarrassed by your harelip?" I asked rather directly.

She seemed to retreat into herself at first, but quickly counterattacked.

"Nobody's perfect, least of all you. Look at you. You wear glasses, you are half bald, and you are not the least bit handsome."

"I know, Sister, and I accept that. But you have obviously not come to grips with your physical imperfections. You're the one who took the pills, not me."

It was better, I thought, to be an internist than a psychiatrist. I was permitted to cut to the heart of the matter, while psychiatrists had to listen for endless hours until the patients saw for themselves the associations and roots of their problems. And only then, if they had insight to see past the defensive barriers they had created, could patients make progress. It was up to the psychiatrist to destroy the armor politely. I could be impolite. Often, patients preferred the direct approach. At least they did in my office.

"Now Sister, I was told you had pain in your abdomen," I said, returning the subject to the reason for my visit. She did indeed have a trivial infection located around the puncture hole where the dialysis catheter entered. It was now slightly swollen but of no real consequence. I figured her complaint was really a ploy. It seemed to me that she was looking for reassurance, for perspective.

"I like talking to you, Dr. Keyloun," Sister said to me as I made ready to leave.

"The feeling is mutual, Sister." I smiled. "But I am not nearly as qualified to listen as Dr. Ratigan. You should really be as direct with him as you always have been with me."

In 1968 it was not easy for people to reveal their homosexual natures, let alone an Italian woman from Brooklyn. Telling her parents she was a lesbian was, for Sister Jean, an insurmountable prospect, especially after becoming a nun. I felt quite confident that Charlie would be able to lead her to understand and come to terms with her demons so that she could lead a happy and meaningful life.

Several years later, Charlie accepted an academic appointment at a prestigious Ivy League medical school. During a visit there with him, we got to talk about this case; of course, he remembered it well. He confirmed that Sister did come to terms with her sexuality but her family never embraced it. She remained a nun.

The Triangle of Abuse

My practice really began to grow in its third year. From seeing two or three patients in a week, I was now seeing ten patients a day, three times a week. A friend or relative referred a random patient, a random patient referred a friend or relative. Someone on the hospital's emergency room staff would send a patient my way. Living close to the hospital helped. Rather than make the long trip into the city from their homes in suburbia late nights or weekends, some doctors preferred to call me in consultation should a hospitalized patient take a turn for the worse. It became generally known that I lived nearby, so I was called on frequently. Likewise, my phone was apt to ring when a surgeon required someone to clear a patient for surgery last-minute. It was a mixed blessing; being so available, I could not escape, and rarely did I have a weekend completely free to myself.

Still, my practice became bountiful. A steady source of referrals developed. A hospital employee, a friend of my wife, informed me that his family physician was about to retire and wanted to transfer the care of some of his patients to a young doctor. Would I be interested? Anxious to not kick a gift horse in the mouth, I agreed. In short order, one of these patients called for an appointment.

Rosina (Tina) Bellini paid her first visit to me the very next week. She swept into my consultation room at a breathless pace, with her coat still buttoned to the neck. When I asked her what was the matter, she began to recite complaints as though she was reading a recipe. It was devoid of emotion, and scripted as if it had been oft repeated. She complained of being harried at work, of being overworked and under appreciated, of not nearly receiving the pay to which she was entitled. She lamented the long commute home after long days in the shop, only to have to cook and clean for her family awaiting her there. Not one word was referable to a physical malady.

"Ah!" she said, barely coming up for air, "it's late. I have to catch the ferry." She promptly stood up, raised her skirt, lowered her panty hose and presented me with her left buttock. "Give me the shot, and I'll go."

"Excuse me? What shot?" I asked, still dazed by the whirlwind that had just blown through.

"Doctor Pastore gave me a B_{12} shot every week. You don't need to examine me. It's not necessary."

It was clear that I was not about to have a dialog with her on this first visit (and quite possibly not even on the tenth), so despite my astonishment, I mechanically gave her a shot of B_{12} and dismissed her. There was no risk involved in giving her the shot, and we had at least begun to establish a relationship, strange as it was.

The following Friday at 5:15 p.m., Tina was back in my office, just as she promised. She was an obligate patient, presenting herself compulsively at the same time each week, and hurriedly leaving to catch the ferry home to Staten Island.

Tina worked as a pattern maker's assistant. My parents and siblings were in the garment industry, manufacturing ladies' bathrobes and lounge-wear, so although Tina boasted the prestige of her position, I was well aware that she ran errands, cut fabric, sewed on buttons, and performed other menial (but essential) tasks. On her salary, Tina was finding it difficult to pay for each office visit. I willingly reduced my fee for her.

As the weeks went by, I insisted on more meaningful communication, beginning with a thorough examination. I extended the interval between her appointments, and soon managed to convince her not to get a B_{12} shot on every visit. There was no medical reason to prescribe B_{12} weekly. Even a patient with pernicious anemia required only a monthly injection. Clearly, her previous doctor was using the red liquid injection as placebo, but for what remained unclear.

Several months went by before Tina casually mentioned to me how much her husband drank. Then she immediately dismissed it as if every husband drinks to excess. "Oh, you know how men are" was a common refrain. In one breath she would complain of his brutish behavior, and in the next she'd either forgive him for it or justify it.

"He work so hard all day, he need it to relax. You know how men are."

Tina had three adult daughters. One had married and moved away with her husband to an island in the Caribbean. The two younger daughters lived at home. When I casually inquired if there were any potential sons-in-law to whisk them away, Tina sucked her teeth and said, "No, no. They don't date. They never bring friends home. At least not for a second visit." She related how her husband would embarrass his daughters with his drunkenness. He would pick on them for the quality of company they kept, or berate them mercilessly in front of the "unsuitable" date they brought home.

"The girls get so mad, but he still tease them. Men!"

Then, he would launch an assault at the boy for any number of trivial reasons, humiliating his daughters even further.

"He worry about his little girl. You know how men are."

Tina never intervened to defend her daughters. If I ever asked her why she didn't, she would look off and quietly whisper, "He'll take it out on me."

I had a dark feeling that something more was going on in her household. One day Tina finally let it slip how often he struck her during his drunken binges. The words had no sooner escaped from her mouth than she swore he didn't mean it. It wasn't his fault. It was an accident.

I listened to Tina's stories at length, knowing there were better ways of treating psychic and physical trauma then with a B12 shot or by bending a physician's ear.

In every abusive relationship there is an eternal triangle: The abuser, the victim, and the enabler. In the Bellini family, all of the women were victims, but Tina was clearly the enabler. By not standing up for her daughters, defending them, and taking a strong position for them, she allowed the chaos to continue. That diagnosis was simple to make. The treatment—getting the family members to recognize and adjust their respective roles in the living theatre that constituted their family life—was much more difficult to implement. Psychiatrists were the best equipped to deliver this kind of therapy, but Tina could not afford the fees, let alone prolonged psychiatric care. It wasn't uncommon for a family doctor like me to serve as a "curbside" counselor for run of the mill problems, so I thought I could still help in my own way.

In short order, I met other members of the Bellini family. Tina approached me about her youngest daughter, Philomena. She was worried because she had become sullen and withdrawn, rarely engaging in conversation. Tina asked if I would be willing to see her at a reduced fee. I agreed, and a few days later, they entered my consultation room together. While Tina always appeared haggard and worn, Philomena provided a glimpse of what Tina might have looked like in her youth. She was twenty-two years old, and her skin was as smooth and pale as alabaster. Her figure was exceptionally well proportioned, and her jet-black hair was combed straight to frame her face. Her eyes were lively and brown. She was neatly but plainly dressed.

I invited Philomena to tell me what was wrong.

"Nothing," she said abruptly. She met my gaze for an instant, then stared out the window. Her brows were furrowed and I sensed her teeth were clenched.

"*Uffa*. Nothing!" Tina interrupted, "She spend all her time in her room, she insolent, she never tell me where she go when she leave the house..."

Philomena shot Tina a glare, her face contorted in a snarl.

I had already heard Tina's perspective on the family problems for over a year. I wanted now to hear it from her daughter herself. Besides, I sensed there was more to it than what Tina was reciting.

"Tina," I said, "why don't you relax for a few minutes with a magazine in the waiting room while I chat with Philomena?"

Nothing momentous transpired that first visit, but I told her that, based on what I had learned from her mother, I thought I might understand some of her problems, and I offered my time to listen to her if she desired. She did. Over the course of several visits, Philomena verbalized a hatred for her father and disgust with her mother. She recognized the role her mother was playing and resented it. It made her angry to hear the bickering, the shouting, the door slamming, the implied sexual frustration, and the recriminations of aborted dreams. But while she was clear on the abuser/enabler relationship of her parents, Philomena did not recognize herself as a victim. She couldn't express why she didn't date or bring friends home. She seemed content to walk through her young adulthood wearing blinders.

When Tina's elder daughter, Edwina, eventually came to see me, she denied any family discord whatsoever. I met Edwina shortly after she had been laid off as a teacher in the public school system. She had not acquired tenure, so during the financial crisis in New York in the 1970s, she was one of the teachers who fell victim to the fiscal axe. Edwina was a few years older than Philomena, about twenty-five. She was not nearly as pretty as her younger sister. Her features were coarser, as if God had been in a rush the day He made her, and had merely placed everything in its approximate location. Edwina had an engaging personality. Her intelligent conversation compensated for whatever she thought she lacked in physical attributes.

She had dreams of climbing up the ladder in the school system, and knew she had the capacity to achieve it. After the layoff, she eventually found employment at a broadcasting company in a secretarial pool. She thought it was a menial job beneath her intellectual stature, and her resentment was in full display. She was furious that the system had let her down, that it had taken away the security of being a teacher and forced her to work at a grubby job in the jungle of Manhattan.

Edwina had many girlfriends, but spoke nothing of boyfriends or dating, other than to dismiss the subject altogether.

"All men want is to get into your pants."

I sensed she was angrier at having lost her job.

When the subject matter turned to her family, however, Edwina could not stress enough how wonderful her home life was. She blithely related how much her mother and father adored each other, and what a nurturing and caring environment they created for her and her sister.

Curious, I thought. *This is a far cry from what I have been led to believe.*

I only saw Edwina occasionally, as one would expect from a normal, healthy young woman. One day, she came to see me for a vaginal discharge. When I told her she had gonorrhea, she was consumed in a flood of tears.

"Please don't tell my parents. Promise me you won't tell them!" she wept.

How could I tell them? More importantly, why would I tell them? Edwina was an emancipated adult, and had every right to privacy.

The source of her venereal disease was none other than a physician she had been dating clandestinely for several years. He lived in Brooklyn, saw her on a regular basis, and was very much married. She could almost let herself believe that she could tell her father she was having an affair. She thought she could talk him through the rage of how "nice Italian girls don't fuck before they're married." She might even survive him finding out about her run-in with the clap. What she couldn't explain to her very Italian father was why she was having an affair with a Jew.

"You have to swear not to tell. I'll be in so much trouble!"

I found her reaction odd. Whereas she was an adult who managed to contract a venereal disease, she was having a completely immature reaction to the diagnosis. It was like an infant caught with her hand in the cookie jar—Please don't tell my daddy! I realized that Edwina carried herself as if she were still a child in her parents' household, actively perpetuating an idyllic fantasy of her home life. It seemed to me that she wanted nothing more than to be loved by her father, and the only way she knew how was to maintain a "Daddy's Little Girl" image and do whatever he said. Confronting her father with such adult issues as these would shatter the very delusion she had of her relationship with him.

Try as I might, in all the years I knew these three women, I could never lead them to any insight into their subconscious motives, or to the position they played in the triangle. My limited psychiatric training was exhausted. I knew what the matter was, but remained unable to effectively treat it.

I referred Tina to Charlie Ratigan and asked him, for her sake, to make a concession on his fee. For my sake, he did. But after several visits with her, he called me and confirmed that Tina was unlikely to ever confront her problems. Her denial was such an amber-hard shell of protection against the hell she was living in that it was impossible for her to see how her behavior was jeopardizing her daughters. She, like so many victims of abuse, convinced herself that what she endured daily was "normal." Her actions and behavior were motivated by a deep-seated masochism. Charlie felt that so long as she was functional, there was nothing more that could be done to help her. As I hung up the phone, I realized I would probably be the curbside psychiatrist to this family for the foreseeable future.

The surprise of my life came one July weekend, when Tina called me at home to tell me that Pasquale Bellini himself was in the emergency room, and asked if would I come see him.

Upon entering the emergency room, the sight of him immediately confirmed what I had imagined him to be all those years. Frankly, he was more than I expected. He was a mountain of a man who looked wider than the gurney he lay on. I introduced myself, and he extended a large, rough, and calloused hand. His face was wide and he had a full head of wavy gray hair. The nose was flat, like that of a prizefighter who fought one too many rounds. I could not discern a neck. He spoke haltingly, almost mumbling in broken English. As he groped for words, he would look to his wife. Tina, true to form, attempted to speak for him, protecting him as she would a wounded, frail child, but I waved her off and insisted on communicating with the patient directly. I lived a lifetime with a brother who stuttered, waiting patiently for him to punch out a word or two. I had no trouble according the same civility to this man. He was a drunk, a bastard, and an abuser by Tina's indictment, but I had no right to accept her judgment as truth. I had listened to Tina and Philomena rant for several years. Now it was time to listen to Pasquale. I needed to assess him with a clean slate.

Unfortunately Pasquale did not oblige me with garrulous conversation. We got right down to the business at hand.

"What seems to be the problem, Mr. Bellini?" I asked.

"The leg. It's cold."

"I thought it better we bring him here," Tina interjected.

I asked him how much he smoked. He told me a pack a day. When I asked him about his drinking, he said, "Only when I eat."

Hmm.

He complained that pain in the calf of his right leg often awakened him at night. He didn't think much of it because he often developed pain in the calf while walking.

Intermittent claudication, I said to myself before I had even examined him. The man had peripheral vascular disease due to arteriosclerosis. I padded my ego with what I thought was a brilliant diagnosis. Get him to quit smoking, the pain will subside, and he'll think I'm a genius.

My daydream ended abruptly when I drew back the sheet to examine his legs. Not only was his right leg cold, but it was also white as a cadaver's. I detected no pulse. I took a deep breath and began to explain the gravity of the situation. To my shock, he refused to stay in the hospital to be studied or treated. No persuasive argument would change his mind. He insisted on going home.

I had a flashback to my days as an intern when a man came into the same emergency room one night with crushing chest pain. His electrocardiogram showed that he was having a heart attack. In fact, the paper strip showed what we commonly called "tombstone T-waves," an electrical sign that portended impending disaster. As delicately as I could, I told the patient he was having a heart attack, that his condition was serious, but with proper care, all would turn out well. I advised him that he needed to be hospitalized, whereupon he leaped from the bed, tore off the electrical leads from his chest, the oxygen mask from his mouth, the intravenous line in his arm, and darted out of the emergency room. As I raced after him down the corridor, nurses and attendants joined me, begging him to reconsider his actions. He fled into the night. About an hour later he was brought back to the emergency room by the hospital's ambulance. The police found him lying on the sidewalk two blocks from the hospital. He was dead on arrival.

As Pasquale gingerly replaced his shoe, I suggested that he at least consult with a vascular surgeon if he had no confidence in my diagnosis. I gave him the name of an extremely competent doctor who had himself emigrated from Italy, figuring there would be an instant rapport that might lead Pasquale to seek the treatment he required. Pasquale said he would go see him.

My hunch proved correct, and a week later, Pasquale was in the hospital undergoing an arteriogram. Contrast agent was injected into his aorta through a catheter introduced through the femoral artery. It outlined a ragged, tortuous aorta and narrowed femoral arteries. On his left side, the contrast agent tapered to a fine line along the inner thigh but then reappeared below the knee, but on his right side, the contrast agent abruptly cut off, leaving only an indistinct blush below the knee, a marker of poorly developed collateral circulation.

By now, the pain in Pasquale's leg was unbearable. Armed with definitive test results, my surgical colleague finally convinced Pasquale to undergo surgery to bypass the blocked artery. Regrettably, Pasquale's arteries were beyond repair. Despite a heroic attempt by a surgeon with the hands of Michelangelo, nothing could be done for his far advanced arteriosclerosis.

I informed Pasquale and his family of the bad news, and collectively reminded them of the deleterious effect of smoking. No matter what the damage, it is always a good time to quit. As I reviewed his chart in preparation for discharge, I read the notes made by the surgical house staff. Pasquale told me he smoked a pack of cigarettes a day and drank only socially, but he admitted to the surgical resident that he smoked three packs of cigarettes and drank no less than a liter of wine and several highballs every day. I could do nothing more than roll my eyes.

Pasquale Bellini (and, to a lesser extent, Tina and her daughters) embodied the ultimate frustration for a doctor: knowing what is in store for a patient, yet being unable to alter the course towards disaster, not for a lack of knowledge, but because the patient is intransigent.

Under and Over

Back in my days as Chief Resident, one of my responsibilities was to answer consultation requests on indigent patients in the psychiatric ward in the Reiss Pavilion. Under the line item "Reason For Request" on the form in Helen Turner's chart was written "Depressed patient unresponsive to treatment." I thought it peculiar that I was called, as I was not qualified to suggest alternative medication to what may have been prescribed by the attending physician. She had been admitted to the psychiatric division of the hospital because she exhibited bizarre behavior alternating with almost absolute emotional withdrawal. I continued to read the chart, and quickly discovered that the treatment referenced on the request form referred not to a course of medication, but instead to several rounds of electric shock therapy. It was clear that I was called for other reasons.

When I arrived at the nurses' station, the young nurse on duty stood to greet me.

"Good morning, Doctor. How may I help you?"

It was a custom at St. Vincent's Hospital that nurses always stood to greet doctors when they entered the nurse's station. It was a sign of respect, and one that I appreciated, especially considering that any of these young women could have been doctors in their own right. The nurses at St. Vincent's were supremely knowledgeable, well-trained and caring. It was their professionalism that separated St. Vincent's hospital from other institutions.

"Good morning. I'm here to answer a consult on Helen Turner."

"Yes, of course. Mrs. Turner is in the sunroom."

She escorted me down the hall to a common area, where I found the patient slumped in a lounge chair, leaning forward and staring into space.

"Good morning, Mrs. Turner. My name is Doctor Keyloun. I've been asked by your doctor to examine you."

I was met with silence.

"Is anything bothering you right now?" She continued to stare.

"Are you in pain?" Nothing.

"Is there anything you want to tell me?" Again, no response. There was no smile, no frown, no visible expression of emotion. It dawned on me that she could still have been in a fugue state brought on by the shock therapy, and the lack of conversation was an aftermath of her treatment.

"Nurse, will you bring Mrs. Turner back to her room so I can do a physical examination?"

"Of course, Doctor," she replied, and then addressed the patient. "Mrs. Turner? Can you walk with me back to you room please?"

I watched as the patient, without response, dutifully stood from her chair, and holding on to the nurse's hand, ambled down the hall to her room. The nurse assisted her to lie supine in bed, and then stood sentinel by the door while I began to examine Mrs. Turner.

I went through a complete examination of her heart, lungs and abdomen. All of her vital signs were normal. I began a neurologic examination. I had her sit at the edge of her bed. She didn't speak, but she complied with my direction. I asked her to follow my finger with her eyes. Moving my finger through six directions in space, I looked for evidence there was something wrong with any of the three nerves that move the eyes. When I moved my finger downward to the floor, there was an unmistakable delay in her eyelids to follow the downward direction of her eyes.

I checked her reflexes. When I struck her biceps tendon, the muscle flexed immediately, but there was a marked delay in the relaxation phase. The same response was elicited when testing her knee jerk reflex. I could almost count the seconds that elapsed until her muscles relaxed.

These clues were strong evidence of an underactive thyroid gland. It only took one day for the results of a corroborating blood test to confirm the extent of her hypothyroidism: her thyroid hormone level was almost undetectable, and her thyroid stimulating hormone was way beyond the upper limit of normal. I started her immediately on a synthetic thyroid hormone. With such blood results as hers, it was imperative to introduce the hormone incrementally, so as to avoid the potential disaster of an over-stimulated heart.

Mrs. Turner began on the lowest dose possible, and she responded immediately. Shock therapy treatments were terminated, and she was discharged from the psychiatric ward. Every two weeks, she returned for examination and to have her dosage increased. Over the course of two months of outpatient treatment, she transformed back into a fully functioning human being. It was like turning up a rheostat on a light switch.

The behavior Mrs. Turner had exhibited was, in fact, a medical consequence of the hypothyroidism, a condition called "myxedema madness." I don't know how (or why) nobody had done a thorough physical workup on her when she presented to the hospital, but the assumption that she was suffering a psychotic breakdown led to unnecessary, drastic treatments. Fortunately, this kind of misadventure did not happen too often, but it exemplifies why every mentally ill patient needs a thorough evaluation by a competent internist before psychiatric medicines or therapies are prescribed.

Early in my practice, one of my patients referred her cousin, John Padovano, to me.

"I don't know if you want him as a patient, Doctor. He's not 'all there,' if you know what I mean." Then, as if to counter her bias, she added, "His father loves him a lot, but he's at the end of his rope."

The family, she told me, were desperate. They had slavishly followed the advice of their local doctor for years, but progress remained elusive. She was unable to describe the problem beyond the vague classification of "not all there," but I agreed to see the patient, and in due time, an appointment had been made.

Two burly men entered my office. It was difficult to tell who was bigger. They both had massive, barrel-chested physiques, were six feet two inches in height, and had thick, wavy black hair. They could have been twins except for the disparity in age. The father, Danny, was fifty-five years old, and John was twenty-eight. Danny was a security guard for a prestigious bank on Wall Street, and because of his longevity and dedication to his job, he was able to get John hired at the firm to do menial chores. Despite its description, it was a well-paying job. Danny was concerned, however, that his son's behavior would eventually get John fired and jeopardize his own employment.

John's problems seemed to start when he was a teenager. During the first two years of high school his grades were exemplary.

"Johnny all the time come home with A on the report card. But then, in the high school," Danny lamented, rocking his hand to and fro, "not so good." He paused, bowing his head, waiting to regain composure. "Then he talking, talking all the time. He make no sense. Yelling in the house. Make his mother crazy."

John's language became a word salad. He stopped speaking in complete sentences, and shouted and screamed about nothing and everything.

His parents took him to their family physician, who prescribed a "new medicine" to calm him down. I asked Danny the name of the medicine.

"Melorol," he replied.

I had a flashback to my childhood in Brooklyn. There used to be a popular ice cream novelty, called the Mello-Roll. Essentially, it was a small, cylindrical block of ice cream served in a specialty waffle cone. When Danny said his son had been prescribed "Melorol," I got the silly mental image of John's doctor treating him with ice cream. It took everything in my being to maintain a straight face.

The drug in question, in fact, was Mellaril (thioridizine), used to treat schizophrenia. The family was first-generation Italian and lived in the Red Hook section of Brooklyn. Pronunciation was not their strong suit.

I made every attempt to converse with John, but to no avail. His answers to my questions were tangential. He was inappropriately loud, talking at me as if our conversation were not in my small consultation room, but in the midst of a boisterous party in a Knights of Columbus Hall. He was trying to be agreeable, but it was clear that he was, indeed, "not all there." He was not hallucinating, nor was he delusional. He was oriented to person, place, and time. But he had a peculiar wide-eyed stare. His face seemed puffy. I examined him thoroughly but found nothing else to guide me further.

While John was dressing, I had an opportunity to speak alone with his father. The family physician prescribed Mellaril some twelve years prior, and provided unlimited refills. Danny knew intuitively that the strong drug had side effects, so he took it upon himself to adjust the dose based on John's behavior. When John was calm, he'd lower the dose. When John was agitated, he'd raise it again. He wanted nothing more than to get his son to a point where he could maintain a productive life and discontinue the drug altogether.

"Did you ever get X-rays done?" I asked, pressing to get more history on John's case.

"No."

"What about blood tests? Did they tell you anything?"

"No, no. The doctor, he no do them."

"He never got blood work done? Why not?"

"He say John young and healthy, so what would they show?"

What would they show, indeed! My friend Charlie Ratigan often recalled Mrs. Turner's case and her misdiagnosis. Would that other physicians knew the perils of assuming that changes in behavior are always the result of a mental disorder. I drew a vial of blood from John and sent it immediately to the lab.

The report from the blood tests I ordered was shocking. John's serum calcium was more than twice normal. Typically, the body maintains a serum calcium level in a precise, narrow range. Even a five to ten percent elevation above a laboratory's upper limit demands a thorough investigation. John's levels indicated there was a major problem in how his body metabolized calcium. His phosphorous level was half the normal value. Together, the results pointed to a diseased parathyroid gland.

I sent him for X-rays. The films of his long bones showed cysts at the distal ends of both his femurs and humerus bones. There was virtually no bone surrounding the cysts. Why they never fractured was anyone's guess. X-rays of his abdomen showed multiple stones in his kidneys.

There was a tetrad we learned in medical school: stones, bones, abdominal groans, and psychic moans. John had them all. I sent his blood to be analyzed for parathyroid hormone. Carol called me with the results.

"Vic, these levels are so high, I can't say I trust the results. This must be a lab error," she mused.

"Not to worry," I replied. "The lab didn't screw up. You've only confirmed how advanced his disease is."

John suffered from hyperparathyroidism. He had been misdiagnosed and mistreated for the better part of twelve years.

The parathyroid glands are a group of glands that regulate calcium metabolism, and are normally situated in the neck behind the thyroid gland. John either had a single tumor of one gland, or all the glands were working overtime. Today, an MRI could easily delineate with precision the size, shape and location of a tumor. But for John, no sophisticated diagnostic procedures yet existed. The assessment could only be made at the operating table. The only treatment was surgery.

John's head and neck surgeon found a single adenoma, which was removed and sent to Pathology along with a biopsy of the bone cysts. The tumor showed the classic features of hyperparathyroidism, and the bone biopsy showed that it was a rare "brown tumor" also classic to the disease. The post-operative course was uneventful. With only a three-inch incision in his neck, John was home in three days.

At John's first visit to my office subsequent to his surgery, I saw a marked change in his demeanor. He no longer had a far-away look. His face was no longer puffy. He spoke more calmly. He felt well. He had long since stopped taking Mellaril. As follow-up visits continued, repeat X-rays of his long bones were taken. The cysts disappeared completely and were replaced by normal bone.

Regrettably, his mental state did not revert to when he was an A-student. He functioned well, he maintained employment, but he had the emotional affect of a child.

It could all have been avoided with a simple blood test.

A Photograph

Edna was a premenopausal businesswoman with a very responsible job. She was single, never married, and had no children. She commuted to Manhattan every day from Bay Ridge, Brooklyn. Sitting across from me in my consultation room, she was neat and business-like, but there was something about her appearance that I could not quite identify. Her features were coarse. Her face was puffy, her nose was wide (as if it had once been broken), and her hands were sausage-like and large. Her skin appeared wrinkled, as if she had been a smoker for many years or had spent endless hours in the sun, but she denied engaging in either activity.

Edna complained of a dull, diffuse, and ill-defined headache. It was present most of the day, but it did not distract her from work, nor did it interfere with her sleep. Her appetite was excellent and her weight was stable. There were no attendant symptoms to suggest migraine headache, nor were there the features of a tension headache. Her physical examination revealed no abnormalities, and neither did her neurological exam indicate a serious problem. Her electrocardiogram, blood profile, urinalysis and chest X-ray were all normal.

When I informed her of the results of her standard lab work, she allowed that she had already seen several doctors who had all said the same thing. At that moment, something struck me. Call it intuition. Call it a hunch. Call it serendipity.

"Edna," I asked, "have you purchased new shoes recently?"

"Why, yes I have. Just a few weeks ago." She looked at me quizzically. "Why?"

"Has your shoe size changed?"

"Yes!" Edna was wide-eyed. "Why do you ask?"

"There is something about your looks that troubles me, but I haven't been able to put my finger on it."

"Is it serious?"

"I don't know." Then I asked for something I had never before asked of a patient. "Do you have a photograph of yourself from five or ten years ago?"

She hesitated for several moments, assessing, I think, whether or not I had gone mad, before replying in the affirmative.

"Would you mind bringing it with you on your next visit?"

When she returned again the following week, she dutifully pulled a full-face photograph of herself from her purse. It had been taken eight or so years prior. I looked at the picture. Now it was I who was wide-eyed. Before I could say a word, she interjected, "It doesn't much look like me, does it?"

"No, Edna, it doesn't. But you just helped me make a diagnosis."

The pituitary gland is often called the master gland, because the nine different hormones it secretes control myriad functions, including ovulation, lactation, cortisone secretion, thyroid secretion, and growth. Each specialized cell within the pituitary gland is subject to forming a tumor, each with its own distinct syndrome. A tumor of the cells that secrete growth hormone produces in adults a syndrome called acromegaly. The terminal ends of the body begin to grow disproportionately. The nose enlarges, as do the fingers, hands, toes, and feet. The skin becomes coarse and corrugated. Because the disease is slow to progress, changes in external features are not noticeable from day to day, so it is often difficult to diagnose.

Edna was well aware that her looks had changed over the preceding eight years, but she ascribed it to getting older, or perhaps being premenopausal. She never discussed it with anyone, and never thought to say anything about it to any of the doctors she had previously seen.

"Edna," I said, "I think you have a tumor in your pituitary gland."

She was incredulous, but at the end of a complete hormonal and X-ray workup, my diagnosis was confirmed. Edna had acromegaly.

There was but one cure for the disease: surgery to remove the tumor. The pituitary gland is located off the bottom of the hypothalamus at the base of the brain, protected by a bony structure called the *sella turcica*. At the time of Edna's diagnosis in the mid 1970s, the surgical approach to the *sella turcica* was from the top of the skull. The front portion of the cranium was removed, and the neurosurgeon plumbed deep within the brain to find the tumor within the pituitary gland and remove it as best as he could. It was a brutal procedure.

As fate would have it, however, a group from Montreal, Canada, published a paper indicating they had perfected a new surgical approach. They discovered that because the *sella turcica* sits just above the nasal cavity, it is more easily (and less invasively) accessed by going directly through the nose. I shared this information with Edna.

"What would you do, Dr. Keyloun?" she asked.

"There are any number of excellent neurosurgeons here at St. Vincent's, and there are equally qualified doctors at New York-Presbyterian, Mount Sinai and New York University, all of whom would take very good care of you."

"Dr. Keyloun," Edna repeated firmly, "what would you do?"

"Edna, if it were me, and someone had to open my skull, I'd get on the first plane to Montreal."

The operation was a complete success. Edna returned from Canada with a detailed operative report. The results of her pre- and postoperative hormone analyses indicated that the tumor had been completely removed. Her symptoms abated, especially her headache. Although she would never revert to her pre-acromegalic appearance, Edna's skin eventually became less corrugated. And her life was saved.

Denial

When two people marry, more than those two individuals are united. In reality, a marriage establishes a union between two families and their friends.

During my courtship with Carol, I was introduced to many of my future in-law's friends. Most were in the restaurant and food business. Joe Mulino had a cold cut emporium in Astoria, Queens, a predominantly Italian and Greek neighborhood. Joe was an expert making sausage and salami. He was so good at it that he supplied many fine restaurants across the city. His wife, Evelyn, was the most gracious woman I had ever known. She could not have been more giving or loving. As a wedding present for Carol and me, Evelyn hand embroidered a tablecloth. It was a gift from the heart and we treasured it.

The Mulinos lived in a modest house in Bayside, Queens. They were the salt of the earth. They entertained lavishly. On many occasions we were invited with Carol's parents to a Sunday feast at their home. Twenty or so guests assembled at a long table in the basement, and the eating and drinking went on for hours and hours. Evelyn prepared every item on the table. The party culminated with the men, who were deep in their cups, singing energetically and off-key some of the traditional songs from their homes in Italy.

After seven years of friendship, and to my utter surprise, Evelyn appeared in my office one day without making an appointment. There was no way I was going to send her away, so I told Rose to somehow squeeze her into the schedule. In short order, she was sitting across from me in my office.

"Evelyn, it's so nice to see you. How is Joe?"

"He's fine. You know, if he's working he has no complaints."

"And what about you. Do you have any complaints?"

"Not really."

"So why did you come to see me?"

"It's my breast."

"What about it?"

"It doesn't look right." Her answers were monotone and devoid of emotion.

"Well then let me take a look at it."

I ushered her into the examining room, gave her a gown to wear after she disrobed, and told her I'd be in to examine her in a few minutes. While waiting for her to get into a gown, I tried to collect myself. I had a premonition that I would see something I preferred not to. As a rule, women do not present with complaints referable to their breast. Most breast cancers are diagnosed by serendipity or by mammography. Their gynecologist is more likely to make the diagnosis than their internist.

I examined Evelyn as I did every patient, by taking her blood pressure and starting with the head, working down. All the while, I maintained polite conversation to mitigate her anxiety. As I lowered her gown, the sight of her right breast took my breath away. It was a rock hard, deformed gargoyle that was plastered, unmovable, against her chest wall.

"How long has it been this way?" I inquired, summoning everything within me not to betray my emotions.

"Oh, three weeks. Maybe four."

"When is the last time you had a checkup?"

"Not for years."

I completed my examination and was only somewhat relieved to note that her liver was not enlarged.

Evelyn had far advanced breast cancer, likely present for over two years. It is inconceivable that she was unaware of the changes in the architecture of her breast during that time. But because there was no pain associated with the deformity, she ignored it.

We humans have many mechanisms to protect our psyche from harm. We insulate ourselves from attack. Denial is probably our most frequently employed defense. That little voice inside that says "this cannot be happening to me." We want to believe it, so we do. We ignore the problem. Nothing terrible happens, so we feel vindicated. Eventually, the day of reckoning comes, and it can no longer be dismissed.

It has only been there for three or four weeks. It's a childish lie, but under the circumstances, totally forgivable. There was no value in confronting Evelyn with the obvious truth that it had been present for years. But she needed to be told she had cancer. I wished it didn't have to be me who told her.

The diagnosis did not shock her. She may have been in denial, but she certainly wasn't ignorant. She asked about her chances for a cure. I told her there was no way to predict the outcome, but it was certain that she needed to have her breast removed before any other treatment could be initiated.

Surgery was performed within the week. Preoperative tests indicated that the cancer had not spread. Although the tests were not definitive or reliable, they gave reasons for optimism. Regrettably, months later her hip began to hurt, and a bone scan showed she had multiple metastases. Chemotherapy was utterly useless. Evelyn died within six months of her diagnosis.

I met Louise Reilly when she was dating Jim Conrad, a general surgeon who specialized in treating burn victims. Jim was a friend and colleague. He was long divorced, and had enjoyed many years living the bachelor's life, until he started dating Louise and the two quickly got serious.

Louise worked as the head of personnel for one of the country's largest national airlines. It was a responsible and demanding job, and a title that few women held, but Louise had somehow managed to break through the glass ceiling. I got a sense of her business clout one day when we went to the 21 Club together after seeing a show. The upscale restaurant was once a speakeasy, but it became a popular watering hole for business tycoons and celebrities. As we entered, the maitre d' almost tripped over himself to greet her. No sooner did we sit at a table by the bar than a waiter brought a telephone to the table and plugged it into a jack behind her chair. The staff could not have been more attentive. I must confess, it was fun to be treated like royalty, even for an evening. Despite her lofty perch in the business world, Louise was a down-to-earth girl and fun to be with. She had a hearty laugh, and she found reason to laugh often. She loved life and lived it fully. Never once did she display any airs of superiority.

The airline elected to move its headquarters to Dallas, and Louise was forced to make a difficult decision. She could either remain in New York to be with her boyfriend, abandoning her position and salary, or she could move to Dallas, which necessarily would terminate her relationship with Jim, as he was not about to give up his well-established practice to move to Texas. Louise chose the latter. We had a nice farewell party for her, wished her well, and thought we'd never see her again.

Two years later, I found Louise standing in my office waiting room. It was a welcome surprise, one that made me realize just how much I had missed her company. I hugged her, thinking she had stopped by to say hello on her way to some other appointment. It was a shock to hear her say she wanted to see me professionally. I tried to reminisce about the fun things we had once done together, but Louise was all business.

"What's the problem, Lou?" I asked.

"It's my breast."

"What about it?"

"It's swollen and it hurts."

"Did you see Jim about it?"

"No," she answered abruptly and with finality. I surmised that the relationship had soured more than I knew, and decided not to pursue it any further.

In my examining room, as I lowered her gown to inspect her breast, I was overcome with sadness. Her right breast was one and a half times larger than the left breast and it was beet red, immovable, deformed, and plastered against her chest wall. She must have seen the expression on my face because she said, "Doesn't look good, does it?"

She knew me well enough to know I was going to be direct.

"You've got a big problem here and you have to take care of it right away."

She lowered her eyes and replied, "That's why I'm here."

"When did you notice the changes?"

"About a month ago."

I wanted to tell her that I knew she was lying. But what difference would it make? She had inflammatory breast cancer, the most lethal form with the worst survival statistics. Forcing Louise to accurately pinpoint its onset wasn't going to change that. Sometimes, it's better to be part of the fiction than to correct it.

Still, Louise was urbane. She rubbed elbows with captains of industry. She had hundreds of people working for her. She knew hundreds of doctors. She could have gone to any one of the famous clinics in America. I'll never know why she sought me out. She had to know I was no authority on breast cancer. Until that office visit, our relationship had been purely social.

Louise had to undergo radiation treatment just to dislodge the mass from her chest wall so that a surgeon could excise it. Then she began chemotherapy. It was all useless. She was dead within three months.

Breast cancer was an infrequent diagnosis in my practice. Sadly, these two cases both involved friends who, for whatever reason, sought me out professionally only after it was too late for treatment. It is difficult for me to comprehend how anyone could be in such denial about their own health, especially when there is such an outward, physical manifestation of disease. I can only guess that the fear of knowing was worse than the knowing itself. That, or the fear of treatment. The only standard of care at the time was radical mastectomy. The breast tissue was removed, along with its underlying muscle. The lymph nodes in the axilla were dissected (leaving the patient with an untreatable swollen deformity of her arm called lymphedema), and later, her ovaries would be excised.

Was the treatment worse than the disease? Did these women think they preferred death to deformity? I don't know, but I am reminded of a lesson taught by my professor of pathology. Dr. Geschickter admonished, "Don't ask what disease the patient has; rather, ask what patient has the disease."

Carol

We had been married for only a couple of months when I awoke in the middle of the night to find Carol's side of the bed empty. I sat up, and in my sleep-induced confusion tried to determine if my wife's sudden disappearance should be a cause for concern. Gathering my senses, I scanned my surroundings, faintly lit by the constant glow of the city filtering through the windows. There was no light from beneath the bathroom door, nor was there any rustling that would indicate a midnight trip to the refrigerator. Concerned, I stumbled out of bed and padded off to search our tiny apartment, only to find Carol tucked in the furthest corner of the hall, curled in fetal position and barely covered by a light blanket.

"What are you doing here?"

"I couldn't sleep."

"Well, can you do your not-sleeping in our bed, instead of lying out here on the floor?"

"I didn't want to wake you with all of my tossing and turning."

"Don't be ridiculous."

Whether it was because I came from a large family, or because my medical training conditioned me to get as much sleep wherever and whenever I could, I have never had a problem with slumber. I could always fall asleep as soon as I closed my eyes, and only the ring of the telephone could rouse me unexpectedly. Carol was not so lucky. Sound sleep was never a part of her existence, and as the years of our marriage rolled on, we would tease and joke with each other about it with the same mock-annoyance that always let us laugh at each others' foibles.

With advancing Parkinson's disease, however, sleeping became a constant issue. Her sleep pattern was totally disrupted, because her tremor prevented her from dozing off, and then would often wake her again in the middle of the night. (A Parkinsonian's tremor is only present when the individual is awake; during sleep, it disappears. But as a person makes the normal cycle from deep sleep to REM sleep over the course of a night, the tremor returns in relation to how close to the waking state the person is. Always having been a light sleeper, this was enough to rouse Carol completely.)

To combat her sleeplessness, she started on Ambien, and the smallest doses were enough to give her a soporific effect. One night, after she had taken her pill and was watching television with me, awaiting drowsiness, she turned to me and said, "Look!"

"Look at what?" I replied.

"My hand. It's not shaking!"

Remarkably, the drug calmed her tremor, and for the first time in a long time, I saw a small ray of hope in Carol's eyes. She thought she had stumbled on a treatment—one that had been completely elusive from the pharmacy of Parkinson's medications she had tried—from a pill that was only meant to help her sleep.

"Do you think I could take it to stop the tremor?" she asked.

"I don't know. Let me see what I can find."

The next morning, I wrote to the company that manufactured Ambien to inform them of the unexpected beneficial effect it had and to inquire if they had done any research with Parkinson's patients. They were not the least bit interested in my observation. In fact, they suggested that I file an adverse side effect report with the FDA.

Still, Carol was desperate for relief.

"Can't I just try it, and see what happens?" she asked.

"You know that's not a good idea, Carol."

She didn't seem to understand that the temporary relief from tremor was merely a result of the somnolent effect of the drug, and I couldn't imagine anyone, let alone someone with her diminished physical capacity, functioning in a constant state of drowsiness.

"I'll only take a little during the day." She began to negotiate with me as a five-year-old might for candy.

"It's a sleeping pill, Carol! What if you take too much?"

"I won't!"

"What if you get a bad reaction?"

"Then I'll stop!"

"What if you fall down and break a hip?"

"I have to stop the shaking, even if it's just for a little while!"

"I don't want you taking Ambien inappropriately," I said firmly. "That's a path to disaster. Don't make me get rid of the prescription entirely." Carol began to sob at the finality of my threat. To her, Ambien was her last ray of hope, and I had crushed it. "Look, sweetheart, I know what you're going through. But there is a right way and a wrong way. There has to be something out there for you. Give me time to find it."

Carol and I shared the same house. We shared the same bed. We socialized with the same people. But we were living in different worlds. I had work, I had purpose, I had reason to get up every day. It is only in retrospect that I truly understand how imprisoning Carol's life felt to her. The emptiness of her home, the gloom of knowing how her illness would progress, the frustration of finding no medicine that helped, the growing pain in her lower back, and the inability to find a doctor with whom she could bond had all brought her to a very dark place.

I did my best to help Carol when she needed it, and likewise did my best to insulate myself from the irrepressible cloud of depression that was enveloping her. But the status quo at home was becoming overwhelming. Until that point, I had respected as best I could my wife's reticence towards psychiatric therapy. I understood that the concept was antithetical to her upbringing. Her father was a hard-working Italian immigrant who never offered a complaint about anything. He raised his family in a household with strict rules. Whatever problems they may have faced, his children were trained to "tough it out" as he had done. Even in adulthood, Carol couldn't escape the idea that therapy indicated a stigma of weakness. But we had clearly reached a crossroads, and I finally broached the subject of seeking professional help.

"You think I'm crazy!"

"No, of course not!"

"All the shrinks I ever met at St. Vincent's should've seen one themselves."

"Maybe so, Carol. But what have you got to lose?"

"What will people say?"

"You don't have to tell anyone, if you don't want to."

"I'll think about it."

It wasn't until the husband of Carol's friend Claire died suddenly that Carol had a change of heart. With all of her troubles, Carol managed to rally herself enough to be available to lend support to her grieving friend. Claire would come to our house, and the two women would sit together over coffee, talking through each others' problems. At some point, Claire announced without shame or apology that she had been seeing a psychiatrist, and that the doctor had been a tremendous help to her.

Carol did not consult me before making an appointment with Claire's doctor. I was thrilled to see her taking initiative in her own care. I was unfamiliar with the doctor to whom I brought her, but I hoped that their session together would finally bring some relief to Carol's predicament.

Carol returned from her appointment with a prescription for a selective serotonin reuptake inhibitor (SSRI).

"What does an SSRI do?" she asked me.

"Didn't the doctor go over it with you?"

"Not really. I did most of the talking. At the end, she handed this to me, like it would instantly solve my problems."

I felt a little like I was dancing on egg shells. I did not want to interfere with or comment on my wife's choice of doctor, nor I did not want anything I said to be misconstrued, so I broadly explained the SSRI as best I could, without delving into the minutia of how the drug was intended to work.

"Serotonin is a chemical compound that is used by the central nervous system to transmit signals from one nerve to another," I began. "Once a signal is passed, the neuron inactivates the serotonin by reabsorbing the neurotransmitter for future use. That's what's referred to as 'reuptake.'"

"Why would you want to inhibit reuptake?"

"Serotonin is also thought to play a significant role in mood regulation. People who are depressed almost universally exhibit depleted levels of it. By slowing the reuptake process, an SSRI allows for higher levels of serotonin in the brain, which are believed to result in improved mood."

The medicine did nothing for Carol. After a few weeks with no improvement, the psychiatrist prescribed a different SSRI, with the same result. Carol returned again, and was once more given a prescription for yet another SSRI. Over the course of six months, Carol tried every SSRI on the market. If ever there was affirmation that insanity is doing the same thing over and over again and expecting different results, this was it. The failure of her therapy only reinforced Carol's negative attitude about psychiatry. She was most reluctant to see anyone else.

I broached the subject again during our annual checkup with our internist (who is also our close personal friend).

"Paul," I asked, "do you know anyone good?"

"Don't bother," Carol interjected. "I can't stand the lot of them."

Paul chuckled and said, "Carol, I don't have much faith in shrinks, either. But there's one guy I know that I think you'll be comfortable with." Paul knew us both so well, and was able to address Carol's reticence without sounding like he was pushing an agenda. Why I hadn't thought to ask him for a referral at the outset was beyond me. My mind must have been elsewhere.

We called and requested the doctor's first availability. On the morning of the appointment, I woke Carol up, helped her to shower and got her dressed. After we had a quick breakfast together, I drove her to meet Dr. Hernandez. Within minutes a bond was established between all of us. I instantly trusted him; he reminded me of Charlie Ratigan, and I liked that he was a no-nonsense guy who seemed to have little use for long-winded explanations for the "why" of mental illness. I suspect that Carol appreciated that as well. They learned much about each other during their first few sessions. The fact that Dr. Hernandez was a first generation American, born of immigrants and raised humbly in New York City, resonated with Carol. His childhood mirrored her own, it helped her to feel that there was common ground between them.

Dr. Hernandez ascribed much of mental illness to abnormal chemistry. Certainly, patients with Parkinson's disease have wildly aberrant chemistry in their brain, and depression is a frequent accompaniment. He prescribed Remeron, a medicine totally unfamiliar to me, and it worked like magic. Within a week Carol was feeling better. Her mood improved, she gained weight and began to look healthier. During each visit, Dr. Hernandez would speak with her briefly, but privately. He would then invite me into the consultation room and ask if I had any questions. I didn't. I never asked what they had spoken about. After several visits, mainly to adjust the dosage and check for side effects, he dismissed Carol, and advised us to return only if something new appeared.

Our lives returned to manageable. I continued my own research on alternatives to medical treatment. Even after leaving practice, I always kept up with the medical literature. Since Carol fell ill, I subscribed to several journals that focused on biotechnology. Up until this point, the traditional procedural options available for patients with Parkinson's were limited to either a thalamotomy or a pallidotomy. Both are invasive and risky surgeries, wherein specific areas of the brain responsible for motion are destroyed. A thalamotomy can relieve tremor, a pallidotomy can alleviate rigidity, but a patient cannot survive both procedures simultaneously, and so must choose one over the other. The results are usually acceptable enough, but there is no turning back. Whatever the result, it is irreversible.

I had read in my literature of new, less destructive treatments being developed. There were reports of anecdotal experiments where fetal tissue was transplanted into the brains of Parkinson's patients with positive effect. Additionally, Amgen, a biotechnology company based in California, was developing a new medical product they believed could mitigate the symptoms of Parkinson's. With promising, innovative treatments like these on the horizon, I didn't think it prudent to advocate that Carol subject herself to an irreversible destruction of brain structures.

Carol's tremor continued to worsen, her rigidity became more profound and she was totally unsteady on her feet, incapable of walking without holding on to something for support. A walker became an essential part of her daily life. In our two-story Colonial home, even though she swore she was comfortable negotiating the stairs by herself, I was deeply concerned about the catastrophic consequences should she trip and fall.

Then a new development surfaced. Every evening, we watched television together before bed. One night, even though she was entranced by the innocuous program on the screen, she suddenly started trembling. Her eyes grew wide as saucers, and she began to scream and cry, flailing her arms about her. It was a terrifying display of raw emotion, and I didn't know what to make of it. No words of comfort could console her. She sobbed uncontrollably, and I thought she might be losing her mind altogether. It finally dawned on me: she was in the throes of a panic attack. I took her by the hand, and as swiftly as I could, led her to our bathroom. I placed her in the shower and opened the faucets. As the warm water cascaded down over her, soaking her hair and matting her thin nightgown to her shaking body, she slowly began to calm. She stopped crying, her breathing eased, and within a minute she was coherent enough again to have a conversation.

"I don't know what came over me," she sniffled. She looked at me with a curious combination of bewilderment and guilt. "It's like a wave. I saw it coming and I couldn't stop it."

It wasn't an isolated incident. The attacks began occurring with alarming frequency, and we returned to Dr. Hernandez for assistance.

"I feel like jumping out of my skin," Carol explained to him. "It's like someone flips a switch and I'm not in control."

Dr. Hernandez confirmed that she was suffering from panic attacks. He prescribed Atavan, a short acting benzodiazepine, which worked very well to keep her calm if she felt an attack coming on and took it in time. Unfortunately, there were countless occasions when she was taken by surprise, and I had to carry her back to the shower stall.

Combined with her worsening tremor, her deteriorating ability to walk, and the ever-increasing pain from her back, these panic attacks made Carol reticent to leave the house. In no time, she became downright agoraphobic, and merely opening the front door of our home could trigger an episode. It was abundantly clear that we could not continue the way we were.

"We can't go on this way," I confided during a casual conversation. "We've got to do something."

"I know," she replied calmly. Her firm, brief, confident answer was the first evidence that she had come to grips with the reality of her illness, especially its progression. Even in the face of the new, debilitating complication of the panic disorder, the antidepressant regimen she was on restored not only her sense of well-being but her ability to think clearly.

I began to discuss with her the alternatives that I had been researching. Positive reports from the fetal tissue experimentation had led the FDA to allow a team in Denver, Colorado to conduct a clinical trial. I asked Carol if she would be interested and willing to take part.

"Where do they get the tissue to put in my brain?" she asked.

"From a fetus," I replied.

"You mean from an aborted fetus."

"Well, yes, I suppose so," I said, trying to mitigate the sting of what I knew to be true.

"How can you possibly ask me to do that? I couldn't live with myself knowing that an abortion was part of the deal."

"Carol, I'm not asking you to do anything. All I'm doing is making you aware of what's available."

Even though we had never really been a demonstratively religious household, I should have been more sensitive to the fact that Carol, who had been educated by the Sisters of Charity through grade school, high school and college, would never accept that kind of treatment, no matter what benefit she might have derived from it.

Amgen's new product was a cell-stimulating factor. The company had already brought to market drugs that triggered the body to grow red blood cells and white blood cells, and now they believed they had discovered a new one to stimulate the brain to make dopamine, the chemical lacking in Parkinson's patients.

Amgen was about to conduct a clinical trial on their product. Early research was promising, but there is always some amount of inadvertent bias when testing a new medication. Administrators are eager for their protocol to work, and participants want so much to be better that they may see improvement when, in reality, there is none. To counter this, information that could lead to bias in the results of a trail is withheld from the patient, the administrator, or both. Half of the participants are given the new drug, and the rest are given a placebo. In the case of a double-blind study, neither the one administering the medicine knows what is being injected, nor does the recipient know what is being administered.

I explained to Carol that not only was the Amgen trial going to be a double-blind study, but it required the surgical implantation of a device into the skull of the participants, through which the product would be injected

"Are you out of your mind?" she bellowed.

"Please, don't kill the messenger!" I implored.

"I can't imagine anyone agreeing to go through all of that, knowing they may only receive a saline injection, instead of the real thing!"

While we continued to search for definitive therapy, Carol's back became a monumental problem. What had long been a random inconvenience for her was now developing into a chronic, incapacitating malady. She could not sit without pain shooting down her legs, nor could she lie down without similar discomfort. She would find minor relief standing up, but the unsteadiness from the Parkinson's made that difficult as well. Walking was agony. At night, when it was time for bed, she would make a painful exodus from the den to our bedroom, leaning heavily on her walker, sweating and gasping as her legs slowly shuffled her the ten yards to the foot of the bed. Exhausted, she would simply release the walker and crash uncontrolled into bed, hoping not to miss it and fall to the floor. She was determined to do it alone, but witnessing the nightly drama filled me with anxiety. *What if she did miss?*

Once in bed, she struggled to get her feet up and under the covers. Had she slept through the night, my sleep might have been sounder. But one of the symptoms of Parkinson's disease is difficulty, bordering on inability, to turn over in bed. It was one of the few typical symptoms that Carol experienced. On many nights I was awakened with a nudge and a request to "roll me over." I didn't mind. It was the screams of pain and the subsequent tears that precipitated the urgency to investigate back surgery.

We were referred to a neurosurgeon who, after MRI and C-T scans, confirmed that Carol had bulging discs impinging on the nerves to her legs. Dr. Rosenfeld recommended a laminectomy to alleviate the problem, and we accepted her advice. As we negotiated a mutually beneficial date for surgery, Dr. Rosenfeld informed Carol that she wanted her to be fitted for a specially designed back brace to be worn during the post-surgical recovery period. I thought the notion strange, as I had never heard anything like it in all the years of my practice. Never had I known any orthopedic surgeon or neurosurgeon to prescribe a brace for surgery on a ruptured disc. *I suppose there is a first time for everything*, I surmised. Perhaps I wasn't as up to speed on the neurological literature as I had imagined.

Someone came to our home to custom fit Carol for the device. He required that she be completely disrobed, save for a nylon garment that he provided. It looked like an oversized leg from a pair of women's sheer stockings, and it "covered" her from her clavicle to just above her knees. Once I helped Carol into the body stocking (which I could only assume was meant to offer a modicum of propriety, regardless of the fact that the constricting fabric was completely transparent), I brought the technician into our bedroom, where I left him taking measurements of her body, while I retired to my home office.

Twenty or so minutes later, I heard the technician leave, and in the ensuing silence, assumed Carol was getting herself dressed. I continued working on whatever it was that occupied my attention, until I heard a noise behind me. I turned around to find Carol leaning seductively against the doorframe. Her face was fully made up with thick lipstick and rouge. She wore nothing but the sheer stocking, but she had adorned it with a gold belt, a brooch and a string of pearls slung down to her navel.

"Hey, Doc," she said in an overly husky voice, "d'you wanna go out sometime?"

It had been such a long road, full of heartache, sorrow, depression, and frustration. Carol's struggle had been so overwhelming, mostly for her, of course, but also for me as her husband and caregiver. There were many times when it all seemed hopeless and bleak, when I feared the woman I knew was gone forever. But here she was again, that girl with whom I instantly fell in love some thirty years prior, squished ridiculously into a nylon stocking, cracking jokes at the absurdity of it all.

The peals of laughter lasted a long, long time.

Surgery went well, but the days following in the hospital were quite eventful. Dr. Rosenfeld came to visit only once, early in the morning the day after surgery. She barely waved her hand before departing again. It seemed she was reassured enough to know that Carol was breathing. She treated Carol like a faulty carburetor; once she deemed Carol fixed, her attention went elsewhere.

Meanwhile, a washcloth and a kidney basin filled with soapy water had been left on the nightstand next to Carol's bed. She had barely awakened from anesthesia, and was apparently expected to sit up and wash herself.

Later that morning, a nurse from the pharmacy, in one hand holding a tray with a small cup and a glass of water on it, shook Carol awake with the other.

"Missus, It's time to take your Sinemet."

Carol sat up, took the oblong yellow pill from the cup, nibbled off a corner, and returned the remainder to the cup.

"Mrs. Keyloun, I have to see you take the whole pill."

"No, I can't take the whole pill at once. I get terrible side effects. Didn't the doctor explain it to you?"

"No, Ma'am, she did not."

"Well, can you speak to the doctor, please?"

"No, Ma'am. The doctor is not available, and you are scheduled to take your medication now. I have to see you take the whole pill."

Knowing that the fight was lost, Carol let out a heavy sigh, put the remainder of the pill in her mouth and swallowed the cupful of water.

"There, see?" The nurse smiled with satisfaction as she headed for the door. "That wasn't so bad, was it?"

Once the nurse turned into the hallway, however, Carol pulled the pill from between her cheek and her teeth and stuffed it into her pillow.

On the second day, the kidney basin—which had been left to fester on the nightstand—was accidentally knocked to the floor. Housekeeping sent an orderly to mop it up.

"I'm glad it happened," Carol told me during visiting hours, as she recounted the day's events.

"Why?"

"At least now," she said with a slight twinkle in her eye, "there's a clean spot on the floor."

That very day a technician from the rehabilitation department came to see her. He applied the custom-fit corset, got Carol out of bed, and walked with her to the end of the corridor. Carol expected to turn around and walk back to her room, but the technician insisted she also walk down a flight of stairs. This was one day after surgery. The technician then demanded that she walk the entire distance back to her room, rather than call for assistance. Carol was about to pass out from the ordeal.

It was difficult for me to be angry. I understood that the pharmacy nurse could not adjust the doctor's prescription, and that she had to see it administered as written. Written orders always have to be followed to the letter, lest the wrath of administration come down on the person who deviates, or takes liberty to interpret them. But why, after Carol and I had both explained with painstaking detail her atypical medical regimen and the horrible repercussions of deviating from that which had taken so long to perfect, was the prescription not written correctly? And, although I'm sure he was doing his best to motivate my wife to push past her comfort zone during post-surgical rehabilitation, it would have taken the physical therapist no time at all to learn that a walk down the hall was more exercise than any Parkinsonian could have handled on a *good* day, never mind while recuperating from the exhaustion of surgery and anesthesia.

Most problems could be avoided if members of the hospital staff just took a few minutes to truly listen to their patients. But I knew well that, even under the best circumstances, a hospital can be a cauldron of chaos, with conflicting interests ruling the day. I was no stranger to any of it. How often had I witnessed, in the rush of practice, doctors making careless mistakes? Selfishness, egotism and appalling myopia were rampant. It hasn't changed. It is an unfortunate and frustrating reality of the profession.

For as much empathy as I had for the system, I still took Carol home the next day. God only knows what else they might have done to her had she remained in that hospital.

The Ambrose Lightship

The Lightship Ambrose stood at the entrance to New York Harbor, serving as a beacon to incoming vessels to the Port of New York. It was so named because it sat at the entrance to the Ambrose Channel, about twelve miles south of Manhattan, and was the first object people saw as they approached New York Harbor. It had a blinking sentinel light and a bell that clanged with every sway of the sea. Since 1823, it warned incoming vessels, and guided them to the channel. I had a patient who told me that she lived with her boyfriend on the lightship. They were, in essence, its custodians, responsible for ensuring the onboard generators remained functioning.

Susan was about twenty-eight years old when she first came to me complaining of an offensive odor emanating from her vagina. Despite her meticulous hygiene, the odor remained. Her live-in lover was put off by it, and it was interfering with intimacy. She had no other complaints referable to her gastrointestinal system besides occasional cramps, which she ascribed to her menstrual cycle. She did not have diarrhea or blood in her stool. She appeared to be in good health, had a good appetite, and didn't use drugs or alcohol in excess. Her physical exam was perfectly normal until I did a pelvic examination. When I asked her to strain, fecal matter oozed from a tiny opening on the rear wall of her vagina. She had a rectovaginal fistula.

We discussed the probable causes for her predicament and the potential treatments. She more than likely had either Crohn's disease or ulcerative colitis. Surgery was definitely likely. Depending on the underlying disease, she would either require a colostomy or an ileostomy. Both procedures divert the fecal stream by bringing a loop of bowel to the surface of the abdomen to empty into an external bag. A colostomy addresses the large intestine, and allows for semi-solid stool, whereas an ileostomy takes a portion of small bowel, resulting in semi-liquid stool.

Susan was a young woman, and the thought of having either surgery was daunting. I wanted her to think about it for a few days before we embarked on a workup to determine the cause of her fistula and a definitive course of action. I made an appointment for her to see me the following week.

That weekend, I was off duty. I signed over my practice to a colleague and looked forward to a few days off without responsibility. Upon my return, I found Susan in the hospital. Apparently, she had panicked about the prospect of feces oozing from her privates and called my colleague, Peter Sessa. Peter was a good physician and a friend, but he did, however, have more of an affinity for the trappings that Medicine afforded him than he did for actually working in the trenches. He liked horseback riding and dressage. He did not like caring for "smelly" diseases or medical complications. He met Susan in the emergency room, and without benefit of a workup to determine the true cause of the fistula, called a surgeon in consultation. The surgeon immediately performed a colostomy, having convinced Peter that the presence of a fistula required emergency surgery, regardless of its cause.

It may be a generalization, but it has been my experience that there are no two personalities more divergent than internists and surgeons. Give a set of circumstances to internists, and they will ponder, scrutinize, and agonize over every possible course of action. Surgeons, on the other hand, will more often than not opt for surgery than for medication, watchful waiting and observation. Granted, they are trained to operate, but sometimes they can be impulsive. Had Susan suffered with ulcerative colitis, the colostomy would have been the appropriate thing to do. However, we had not yet conducted a thorough workup to determine the cause of her fistula.

Several weeks later, during her convalescence from the colostomy, Susan began to ooze a brown watery substance from an area on her buttock, approximately an inch adjacent to her anus. She had developed a second fistula. The best diagnostic tool we had was a rigid proctoscope, a forerunner to the fiberoptic colonoscope, that could be inserted only about twelve to fourteen inches into the rectum. The portion of bowel visible to the proctoscope appeared normal, except for an inflamed area just within the anus. It wasn't until she was well enough to undergo a full gastrointestinal series that we were finally able to see several areas of diseased bowel in her small intestine. She had Crohn's disease.

Not much was known about Crohn's disease, but all the experts agreed that, in the presence of a fistula, the only reasonable treatment was to divert the fecal stream. It was universally accepted that something in the fecal stream contributed to the mayhem in the bowel. Fistulas would never close spontaneously or with surgery as long as feces continued to pass by the lesion. Unfortunately for Susan, she would have to undergo a second surgery; she required an ileostomy, after all. The hastily scheduled colostomy had been a waste of time, resources and energy.

We discussed the findings with Susan and she accepted them with remarkable equanimity. The idea was to bring to the surface of her abdomen the segment of normal bowel nearest to her stomach. Hopefully there would be many feet of normal bowel, so she would not have to suffer with malnutrition or vitamin deficiency syndromes.

On the day of surgery, at about nine o'clock in the morning, I was urgently paged to call the operating room. The surgeon requested that I come to the operating room at once. I scrubbed as quickly as I could, and donned the requisite gown and mask. As I entered the operating room, the surgeon looked at me and I could see in his eyes that he was troubled.

"Your lady has big problems."

"I know. That's why she's here in your bailiwick."

"No. I mean here in her abdomen. She has multiple fistulas, mostly bowel to bowel."

"Unbelievable. She has no G. I. symptoms to speak of."

"The nearest proximal bowel is only two feet from the Ligament of Treitz."

The Ligament of Treitz is an anatomical landmark that identifies the very first part of the small bowel beyond the duodenum. No one has survived with such a minimal length of bowel. We were between Scylla and Charybdis. If we did nothing, her disease would progress with inevitable infections, fistulas, and a miserable quality of life. If we elected to do the ileostomy, we were in uncharted medical waters. I believed we had no choice. I suggested we proceed with the ileostomy. The procedure was performed, and she was returned to her room and fed intravenously until the ileostomy had sufficiently healed to allow her to eat.

The normal progression of feeding a postoperative patient starts with clear liquids, then to semi-solid food, and finally to a regular diet. Susan no sooner swallowed her first sip of apple juice that it found its way into her ileostomy bag. Within minutes of eating scrambled eggs, they appeared in the bag, looking as if they had just come from her plate. Like an express train, everything she ate ran directly through her stomach and the two feet of small bowel. Nutrition was going to be a major problem for her.

We had to figure a way to slow the transit time in her bowel to allow some absorption of nutrients. Fortunately, Immodium had recently been introduced into the market. The drug was intended as a treatment for diarrhea. We prescribed it to Susan with remarkable success.

She also benefited from the Space Program. When man first went into orbit, the common question people had was, "How do they go to the bathroom in space?" The answer came from newspaper reports that NASA had formulated a special diet that provided astronauts with sufficient caloric intake with virtually no bulk. The diet resulted in little to no defecation. It was called an elemental diet. We petitioned NASA and told them of our patient's rare predicament. They graciously offered to supply her with the space diet. In the subsequent weeks, Susan did extremely well, and eventually returned with her live-in lover to the Lightship Ambrose. That would ordinarily be a satisfactory ending to a tragic story. It wasn't.

Several weeks later, Susan appeared in the emergency room. Her boyfriend, who seemed overly solicitous, accompanied her. She was bleeding from the edges of her ileostomy. The small bowel was torn from the edge where it had been stitched to the abdominal wall. She denied trauma. She said she didn't fall. She swore she took meticulous care of the surgical site, washing it as directed and applying the prescribed medications. The surgeon who performed the procedure was called in to consult but would not be available for several hours. So Susan was admitted to the hospital to await his opinion as to how to fix the problem.

When Susan arrived in her room, we were able to speak in the absence of her boyfriend. I asked her again how her ileostomy had been damaged. She broke down in tears, sobbing uncontrollably. Her remorse was palpable and pathetic. It seems that her boyfriend had found something erotic about it. He made love to her (if that is what anyone can call it) through the tiny opening in her abdomen instead of her natural organ. His penis had violently disturbed the anatomy. It was a blessing that what little normal small bowel she had left was not ruined by his bizarre behavior. I never had the opportunity to ask him if the aroma of feces from her vagina had so turned him off, how he could try to insert his penis into a stoma that oozed constantly.

The surgeon was able to reconnect her bowel with the skin of her abdomen. Luckily, it did not get infected. She made an uneventful recovery and returned to the lightship.

I never saw her again.

Asking the Right Question

Gerry was a thirty-four year old man who came to me with a vague complaint. He said he didn't feel well. He hailed from a town on eastern Long Island and had seen many local doctors, none of whom could establish a diagnosis. One of them suggested that he check himself into Mount Sinai Hospital, where top-tier doctors could evaluate him. He followed the advice, and was thoroughly evaluated. After numerous visits and multiple tests, he was discharged from the clinic with the suggestion that his problem was psychosomatic. Finally, one of his dear friends referred him to me. Gerry felt he had nothing to lose (and he didn't want to test the friendship), so he came to see me. We were about the same age at the time, and I suspected that he wasn't quite sure I was competent or seasoned enough to discover what was wrong with him. After all, if the doctors at Mount Sinai couldn't get to the bottom of his complaint, how would I?

I began by trying to establish a chief complaint. It was no easy task. He complained of a vague ill feeling in his abdomen. He could not pinpoint the source. The feeling was diffuse. He described a vague ill-defined queasiness. He gestured by rotating his hand around the area of his navel. He was not constipated, nor did he have diarrhea. His bowel movements were normal and regular, and his stools were formed. His appetite was fine, and he had no difficulty with any food group. His symptoms had been present for almost two years, but they had become more intense over the past six months. He complained that the ill feeling sometimes made him so tired that he couldn't get through the day at work.

His symptoms pointed to his G. I. tract, but I was still unsure what organ system was in play.

Gerry seemed to be well grounded. He had a good job. He was married, in a stable relationship. He was affable, easy to talk to, and respectful.

116

He appeared to be in good health. There was no reason to believe he was neurotic.

I always felt that if a person was willing to give me money to find out what was wrong with his body, then I had an obligation and a duty to do so. It would have been much simpler to tell Gerry that I had no idea what was wrong with him and send him on his merry way, as did the clinicians at Mount Sinai. But I didn't. I resurrected the Jaegers formula. I began with a review of systems.

When I got around to the urinary system, the most curious thing happened. I asked him if his urinary stream was strong. He responded affirmatively. Then I asked if he could start his stream at will. Again he responded affirmatively. Could he stop his stream at will? The latter questions are usually posed to elderly gentlemen suspected of having a large prostate gland, but I asked them nevertheless. He then volunteered a most interesting aside. He said, "You know, when I pee, I pee strong, but at the end of it I sometimes hear 'pfut-pfut.'"

I looked at him quizzically. I never heard a patient say anything like this before.

"What do you mean by 'pfut-pfut'"?

"I don't know. But I thought I'd tell you because you're the only doctor who has ever asked me questions like this."

What Gerry was telling me was that he was expelling air from his urinary bladder. There are only two causes for pneumaturia. Either his bladder was infected with a gas-forming bacteria, or he had a communication between his bladder and intestines. Gerry was not diabetic, and he did not complain of burning on urination. On inspection, his urine was perfectly clear, which presumptively ruled out a gas-forming bacterial infection in his bladder. The more likely diagnosis was that he had a fistula, an abnormal communication between his bladder and a section of his intestine. There are two principal causes for that; ulcerative colitis and Crohn's disease. He did not complain of diarrhea or bloody stools, so the diagnosis tilted toward Crohn's disease. Proving that diagnosis would be another issue.

When I discussed my differential diagnosis with Gerry, he seemed relieved. He seemed happy to know there was a real reason for his feeling ill, even though that reason might turn out to be a serious malady. I told him the first step was to take an X-ray of his abdomen when he had a full bladder. The image showed a gas bubble sitting at the dome of his urinary bladder. Next he had an intravenous pyelogram. A contrast agent was injected into a vein that found its way to the kidneys, where it was excreted. In doing so, the outline of the entire urinary system could be seen. There appeared to be no abnormality and, on this exam, no air was seen in his bladder. Then Gerry had a cystoscopy. A metal tube was inserted in his penis while he was under general anesthesia. Through it, the urologist could visualize the interior of his bladder. He discovered a small puckered area at the dome of the bladder that was inflamed. He made no attempt to take a biopsy, as he could not be certain of its cause. Since we suspected Crohn's disease, he didn't want to make the situation worse than it already was.

We discussed all the findings that had been accumulated. The puckered area in his urinary bladder augured for a fistula. I next had him obtain an upper G. I. series with emphasis on the small bowel. It revealed a narrowing in his distal ileum, the furthermost segment of his small bowel just before it connects to the large bowel. The pathology seemed to be limited to that one segment. Often when dealing with Crohn's disease, by the time a fistula has formed, there are multiple segments that are involved. It was unusual to have just one isolated segment and for it to create a fistula. However, the pathology was present in a classic area, the terminal ileum. The original term employed by Dr. Crohn was regional ileitis.

As little as is known today about the exact cause of Crohn's disease, much less was known in the early 1970s. There was no treatment for the disease itself. Instead, treatment was directed at the symptoms: control of diarrhea, vomiting, and fatigue, if these were present. In Gerry's case, the presence of a fistula could not be ignored. It could go on to infect his bladder, or the disease could progress to develop multiple fistulas. We believed that removing the diseased segment of bowel and severing the fistula would go a long way to making him feel better. There was a risk in that Crohn's disease is notorious for worsening after an abdominal surgical procedure, even if the surgery has nothing to do with the bowel. Operating on Gerry could create a firestorm of new activity, with all the resultant complications. Gerry chose to take the risk, and opted for surgery.

Under general anesthesia, a two-foot segment of bowel was removed with its attendant fistula. The diseased area was excised and the dome of the bladder sutured closed. His recovery was uneventful. Gerry came to see me twice a year for check ups and remained symptom free for five years. He found the trip from eastern Long Island arduous and elected to be followed by a regional doctor. I wished him well. I never saw him again.

Dr. Crohn, for whom the disease is named, made his discovery at Mount Sinai Hospital, a hospital that was considered to be the world's authority on the disease. It is curious to me that Gerry's case wasn't discovered there, or why they were unable to ask the right questions. Our professors at Georgetown told us repeatedly, "Listen to your patients. They will tell you their diagnosis." Only later in private practice did I appreciate those words. People are reluctant to volunteer information. More often than not, they are fearful of being labeled neurotic, especially if the symptoms are unusual. A good diagnostician necessarily must ask questions.

Now that I sit at the opposite side of the desk from the doctor, I bear witness to how the practice of medicine has changed. In any doctor's office, a clerk invariably provides a sheet of paper with a checklist. It asks, "Have you had any of the following?" A laundry list of symptoms and diseases is provided as a substitute for speaking with the doctor. It is beyond impersonal. It is also useless. Is it any wonder why patients today get shuttled from one doctor to another to arrive at a diagnosis? A checklist could never have uncovered a "pfut-pfut."

Sleeping Beauty

Even while she lay in a coma, her face was radiant. Her eyebrows were penciled thick and her lashes darkened with mascara. Her aquiline nose, almost imperceptibly upturned, was that of a CoverGirl model. Even without lipstick, her mouth was deeply pink, and looked as if it had been painted on a pale white canvas. Not a single blemish marred her skin, which was so pale as to almost be transparent. Her hair looked as if she had just stepped out of a salon. Each auburn strand was combed and waved, upswept, and rolled into a French twist. She appeared to be in her forties, but I could not be certain by the way she was groomed. She looked like a mannequin, but her limbs were as limp as a rag, and it wasn't until I touched her and felt the warmth of her body that I thought that this whole episode was an elaborate hoax.

It was Saturday morning, and I was enjoying the luxury of a late breakfast with Carol when the telephone rang. On the other end of the line was Dr. Bob Wilson, a physician on staff at Doctor's Hospital on the Upper East Side of Manhattan. It seemed my name had come up in conversation with a mutual professional acquaintance. Dr. Wilson had a troubling case on his hands, and no one at Doctor's Hospital was able to provide any insight. He asked if I would come and examine his patient. I was, of course, very flattered, but I was reluctant to oblige him.

"Bob, I'd love to help, but I'm not on staff at Doctor's. You know what a hassle the application process is. I really can't get involved in that right now."

"I'll take care of it," he reassured me. "I'll call you back as soon as it's done."

I was enjoying the last sip of my coffee when he called again to assure me that he had facilitated all administrative details. I promised that I would drive up in about two hours, as soon as I had completed rounds on my own hospitalized patients.

Bob Wilson was a society physician, and Society loved him. He was urbane, handsome, and athletic. His physique belied a man in his sixties. The gray-white hair about his temples lent him an air of maturity (and its accompanying wisdom) so admired by his patients. We met in the lobby and introduced ourselves, whereupon he ushered me to the elevator. He briefed me on the case. He had made a house call at his patient's penthouse apartment on Madison Avenue and Sixty-Third Street, and found her in a semi-stuporous state. He immediately admitted her to the hospital, and shortly thereafter, she slipped into a coma. She had been asleep for four days, and nobody could determine why.

Doctor's Hospital was a clean, but old and shabby place. We got off the elevator on the tenth floor, the floor set aside for wealthy patients who could afford better accommodations. As we walked down the hall, it was my immediate impression that not even this private floor looked any better than other hospitals I had seen.

Dr. Wilson led me into the room where Sleeping Beauty lay.

My examination provided no immediate clues. It seemed that all I should have to do was shake her gently and she would awaken. Dr. Wilson, seated in an easy chair in the corner, watched me run through my ritual and leaf through the chart. I glanced at the first page and took note of her name, Jacqueline Harnett. It made no impression on me. Neither did the results of her laboratory tests. When I closed the chart, Bob stood up and asked, "Do you have any ideas?"

"I really don't. This is a puzzling case. Had she ingested the usual junk—barbiturates, chloral hydrate, or some other hypnotic sedative—she would have already metabolized them over the past four days." Wilson nodded as if he had already considered this sequence in deductive reasoning. "We know she didn't overdose on morphine or its congeners for that same reason." His head bobbled on his beefy neck. "It's unlikely that she had a stroke or a subarachnoid hemorrhage, since the neurologic exam was negative. She doesn't have a fever and her white blood count is normal, so meningitis or encephalitis are only remote possibilities, but we should do a simple lumbar puncture to exclude the possibility."

"You're going to have to convince her husband to let us do a spinal tap," Wilson blurted.

"Let's go talk to him. He won't bite us, will he?"

"Don't you know who her husband is?" I shook my head. Dr. Wilson continued, his voice almost reverential, "Benford Harnett!"

"Who is he?"

"My God, lad! Do you live on the moon?"

The light dawned. Benford Harnett was an industrialist and one of the richest tycoons in America. Names such as his appeared in newspapers. Men like him earned mention in history books. Now that I was involved in the care of his comatose wife, I instantly leapt from being a traditional neighborhood doctor to rubbing elbows with one of America's icons. Trying hard to remain unflustered, I straightened my tie, buttoned my jacket, ran my fingers through my hair, and followed Bob Wilson to the waiting room to meet the modern-day Midas.

I expected to see a rotund, graying executive in a blue pinstriped suit. Instead, a surprisingly lean man in his fifties stood to greet me. Benford Harnett was six feet tall, but gave the appearance of being taller. He was muscular, trim, and was dressed in a brown tweed sports coat over a beige turtleneck sweater. His hair was full and parted on the left. His rugged, tanned face made me think he should be dashing out to play polo or go sailing.

Once we were formally introduced, I began my recitation of the facts, and offered my opinion as to what was not the cause of her coma.

"Mr. Harnett," I concluded, "now we need to start thinking about what *is* causing the coma. I think it's highly unlikely, but viral meningitis and encephalitis are remote possibilities. I would like to rule them out definitively, but that would require a spinal tap, and I need your consent to proceed."

Perhaps a minute of silence passed before he spoke. He straightened, expanded his chest with a deep breath, and said in an almost paternal tone, "You seem so knowledgeable, Doctor, and I trust your judgment, but would you indulge me once by discussing my wife's illness with Dr. Michael DeBakey?"

"Of course," I assented, as if Dr. DeBakey and I had each other's telephone numbers on speed dial and conversed regularly, when in fact, Benford Harnett was asking me to call on a medical god for approval. I didn't mind. In fact, I was ecstatic to think that I had a reason to talk to such an eminent American physician. Actually, I knew that DeBakey was Lebanese-American, and I wondered in those moments of heady fantasy if we would commiserate about our Middle-Eastern origins.

"Mr. Harnett," I continued, refocusing my thoughts, "Dr. DeBakey is a renowned vascular surgeon, but I am not sure what he will have to offer to your wife's neurological issue. Why is his opinion special to you...?" My voice trailed off as I noticed Benford Harnett's puzzled expression.

"Because he replaced my wife's aorta, and I respect his opinion very much."

My face must have paled. Surely I should have seen a midline abdominal scar when I examined the patient! How could I have been so careless or oblivious?

Trying desperately to maintain my composure, I said, "Of course, Mr. Harnett. I understand. But since Dr. DeBakey doesn't know me, perhaps you should contact him first and alert him that I will be calling?"

"I'd be happy to," he agreed, and retreated to the elevators to make the call from the pay phone in the hospital lobby.

As the elevator doors closed behind him, I turned to Wilson. "You never told me that she had surgery by Michael DeBakey!"

"I thought you knew," he confessed.

"It's not in the chart, and I don't have a crystal ball! Let me go back and reexamine her abdomen." I had to make sure I hadn't made a fool of myself by missing the surgical scar.

I drew back the sheets and lifted her nightgown to see a virgin abdomen. I thought I was losing my mind, until I looked closer at her pubic hairline. There, at the border of her escutcheon, in the crease of the abdominal fold, was the faintest scar of a Pfannenstiel incision. This is the incision used for Caesarean sections on women who wish to continue wearing bikini bathing suits. I never dreamed an aortic resection could be done through such an incision. But then, I had never taken care of Jacqueline Harnett, and I was no Dr. Michael DeBakey.

I looked up at Bob. "Why'd she have the surgery?" I asked.

"Jackie had been complaining of cramps in her calf. She had seen a number of physicians about it, but none was able to help. When she saw DeBakey, he found an anomalous aorta and suggested it be replaced."

"Did surgery alleviate the cramps?"

"No. It didn't seem to make any difference."

"Is she treating the cramps with any medications?"

"I haven't prescribed anything."

Later that evening, I called Dr. DeBakey from my apartment. He picked up the phone on the second ring. My conversation with him was a virtual repetition of the conversation in the waiting room with Benford Harnett.

Dr. DeBakey asked me no questions and offered no advice. He merely suggested that I do whatever I thought was in the best interest of the patient. After all, he was in Texas, thousands of miles away, and I was her physician. He couldn't have been more gracious. This eminent vascular surgeon with a world-renowned reputation treated me like a colleague, and spoke to me as if we had known each other for years.

The spinal tap was negative. The repeat laboratory tests were negative. I took a sample of her urine and sent it out for thin-layer chromatography, in hopes of finding chemical traces in the sample. It, too, came back inconclusive. The mystery continued, and Jackie slept on.

I was seeing Jackie every morning before work. I'd return to St. Vincent's, make rounds at my hospital, hold office hours, and attend to my other customary responsibilities. At the end of the day, I would travel back to Doctor's Hospital to follow up on Jackie. After a few days of making these bookend rounds, I was exhausted. It quickly reached the point where there was nothing further I could do for her at Doctor's Hospital. They did not have a sophisticated laboratory. Worse, I only had consulting privileges. Whatever I suggested had to first be reviewed by Dr. Wilson, who then wrote the actual orders in the chart. The time it took for me to implement an order was inefficient and not in the best interest of the patient.

"Bob," I said one morning during my consult, "I think Jackie belongs in St. Vincent's Hospital."

"Why?" he demanded.

"Because there's nothing more I can do for her here."

He turned to me and screamed, "You've got some goddamned nerve!"

"What are you talking about?"

"You're trying to steal my patient!"

I took him by his lapel and dragged him to the corridor. "She may be in coma but I don't think we should be talking like this at her bedside." When we got outside of her room where there was no one to witness his tantrum, I said, "Are you crazy? What's this all about?"

"You're here because of me! I cannot believe how ungrateful you are! You would never have met people like the Harnetts without me!" he spat.

I was speechless.

His face flushed red and his hands clenched as he looked me straight in the eye. "You take her to St. Vincent's and I can't bill for my services."

My shock at his outburst contrasted sharply with how calmly I said, "OK, Bob, keep her here. When she dies, you can tell Benford Harnett the news. I've got patients to see."

Within the hour, an ambulance arrived to take her away.

I wasn't sure what more I was going to do for her at St. Vincent's, but I felt more comfortable because I could see her often each day. In desperation, I ordered dialysis, assuming she had a circulating toxin. Admittedly, it was less than a sanguine idea. I did not know the toxin, dialysis has its own inherent potential complications, and the procedure might ultimately be for naught. On balance, the option of doing nothing far outweighed the possibility of irreversible complications. I canceled the order.

Primum non nocere. First do no harm. Hippocrates.

It was at one of those happy-hour bull sessions when, after a few high-balls, random gossip illuminated the situation. I met Carol at McGowan's, a tavern on Greenwich Avenue often frequented by the medical staff. It was a special place for us as it was there that I had given Carol her engagement ring.

Carol was accompanied by a few of her laboratory cohorts, and they were lamenting the new assistant director of the chemistry lab. I couldn't blame them. Suzanna Levinson was a shrew and a conniving bitch. It was clear that she was after her boss' job from the minute she entered the laboratory. Her every action seemed dedicated to sabotaging or upstaging the placid director. Her behavior rankled the laboratory staff, because the discord she created was antithetical to the cohesive unit the lab had always been.

When she came to St. Vincent's, Suzanna had brought with her a new machine called a gas chromatograph. It was still somewhat experimental, and only she knew how to use it. She had been actively recruiting technicians to train on the machine since her arrival, but everyone on her staff had demurred. The technology was an exciting advance that everyone was eager to learn, but not at the expense of having to work for Suzanna. Frustrated by what she perceived as an unprofessional lack of interest, Suzanna had just issued an ultimatum to my wife: either assign a technician, or Carol would have to run the machine herself.

This was the conversation into which I had inserted myself. After several drinks, tempers calmed down enough for me to ask a few pointed questions. For as much as I sympathized with Carol's predicament, I was intrigued by the gas chromatograph and its possibilities. What was especially exciting to me was the machine's ability to positively identify which chemicals were present in a sample of blood, even in minute quantities. It was like examining a fingerprint; each chemical had its own signature. It was much more precise than TLC. I began to imagine the possibility that it could give me a way to account for Jacqueline's profound sleep.

We talked and laughed over several more drinks until each of us departed the tavern to return to our respective homes. Carol and I went for a long walk through Greenwich Village. We approached a restaurant that was new to us on West Fourth Street and decided to try it. An oak bar ran the length of the far wall of the dining room. Crystal-clear mirrors behind the bar created the illusion of a larger room. At the center of each table was a single rose in a bud vase, illuminated from above by a dedicated spotlight. Brass sconces jutted from the bare brick walls. It was a perfectly delightful Bohemian pub, and we enjoyed a delectable meal together.

Carol and I made it a habit of rarely talking medicine at home, and almost never when we were socializing. On our free time, we generally preferred the company of nonmedical people, so as not to allow our conversations to consist of nothing but shop talk. This evening's bull session at McGowen's had been a departure. And as we waited for coffee, I extended the departure further by asking for more information about gas chromatography. In exasperation, Carol said, "Send me a sample of blood. I'll run it myself. But you owe me big time if I have to deal with the bitch in the lab."

I smiled at her, took a last sip of wine, and said, "You give me an answer and you can name your present."

The next afternoon, instead of Carol, it was Suzanna who called me. Even over the telephone, I could sense that she was wearing her gloating, know-it-all, vaguely menacing, Cheshire Cat grin. She insisted on giving me the results in person, so we met outside the patient's room in the intensive care unit. Suzanna began by telling me how hard she had worked to come up with the results. She went on to complain that she, the most knowledgeable chemist in the hospital, was given so little respect and that no homage was paid to her genius. Before she could bore me further with the self-aggrandizing diatribe, I interrupted her.

"The results, Dr. Levinson, please! I have patients to see."

"Oh, yes, the results. Your patient is a junkie."

"You found heroin?" I exclaimed. "That's impossible. She's been in a coma for a week. Heroin would have been metabolized. And, besides, her pupils have been mid-sized, not pinpoint."

"I didn't say I found heroin, did I?" she rejoined haughtily, her nose at an angle a few degrees higher than it was before. "She has quinine in her blood, and quinine is used to cut heroin on the streets."

She was speaking to me as if she were raised in the South Bronx and had intimate knowledge of how drug dealers adulterated their products, when in fact, her knowledge of "the streets" and illegal drugs was superficial at best, and acquired, I suspected, mainly from coffee-klatches and gossip. While quinine may have been found in Jacqueline Harnett's blood, Suzanna's presumption about its source was incorrect and reckless.

"Well, Dr. Levinson," I said, "thank you for your help." I turned and headed to the elevator.

The elevator doors opened, and before I could step on, a single person emerged. It was Benford Harnett. I took him aside to a lounge and invited him to take a seat. I explained how we had found elevated levels of quinine in her blood, and that it was likely the cause of her coma. Now that we had identified the source of the mystery, the solution was relatively simple. What Jackie needed was acidification of her blood to clear the quinine through her kidneys.

"Before I go get this started, Mr. Harnett, are you sure your wife didn't have access to any medications?"

"Well, now that you mention it, Doctor, when Jackie first started having the cramps in her legs, her doctor gave her Quinam. But as far as I know, she stopped taking it after her aortic surgery."

Quinam, as its name might suggest, is a quinine-based drug. Combined with aminophylline, it was often prescribed for nighttime cramping, but was only somewhat effective for relieving symptoms. I suspected that Jackie hadn't stopped taking it, as Benford thought.

I put in a call to the hospital pharmacy and ordered a salt solution of ammonium chloride to be delivered by intravenous drip. The pharmacist was not happy. Because ammonium chloride is not a solution typically stocked, my order required the pharmacy to actually mix the solution by hand, rather than pull it from a shelf.

"Doctor, we simply don't have the time."

"Make time! We are not dealing with a trivial matter. My patient is in a coma."

A long sigh ensued. "I don't think we have sterile ammonium chloride."

"Perhaps I should call Sister McOwen."

It was a subtle threat to involve the laboratory's administrator, but overcoming inertia can sometimes be a challenge.

Several hours later, we started the intravenous drip, which was to run over a six-hour interval. When I left the ICU that night, Jackie was already moving her extremities. In only four short hours, she had begun transforming from a motionless mass to a spontaneously moving (albeit sleeping) human being.

The next morning, I couldn't wait to get up to the tenth floor. Damn the elevators! They were so slow. I would have walked up ten flights, but I knew how out of shape I had become, so I waited, increasingly frustrated with each passing second, for the cursed elevator. I entered the patient's room to be greeted by a most beautiful woman sitting up in bed, wearing a pink nightgown trimmed in lace, her hair combed, her makeup fastidiously applied, and her eyes fluttering. In an accent reminiscent of my wife's Parisian cousin, she asked, "Who are you?"

"I am your doctor," I said and introduced myself.

"But you are so young."

Benford Harnett began to laugh. He was exhilarated. Frankly, so was I. I laughed, too, the anxiety of that week quickly melting away.

Jackie filled in the blanks as we reconstructed the events leading to her coma. It seemed that Jackie had continued to take the Quinam without Benford's knowledge, because she thought they were innocuous pills. For reasons that were not clear, the pharmacist never questioned so many refills. The continued use of the drug caused Jackie to become confused. She would forget whether or not she took her pills, so she would take another to be certain. The normal alkalinity of the blood tends to delay the excretion of quinine. With ordinary doses, this is of no consequence, but in Jackie's case, the massive amount of quinine in her system frustrated any attempt by her kidneys to handle the load, and she eventually lapsed into a coma.

Benford's gratitude was effusive. He spoke kind words about me to any doctor to whom he was introduced. He praised me in particular to the Chief of Medicine. During a tour of the hospital, I took him through the chemistry laboratory. I wanted him to see the machine that saved his wife's life (Suzanna was mercifully at lunch when we made our tour). At that moment, Benford offered to donate eight thousand dollars toward any research project I had in mind. It was a most generous gift, eclipsing anything I could ever have imagined (remember, my fee for an office visit was fifteen dollars). There was absolutely no way to express my gratitude, so I simply thanked him and assured him the money would be put to good use.

The check was made out to St. Vincent's Hospital for tax purposes. The letter that accompanied the gift stipulated that the money was to be spent at my direction. Not many attending physicians were conducting research at the time, and fewer still were able to obtain grant money because their academic credentials did not warrant it. My grant was a total fluke, and it rankled the members of the research committee to the core.

Year after year, I submitted a protocol for a project, only to have it rejected. The committee held veto power over any project that used hospital resources or recruited hospitalized patients. If the committee did not sanction a protocol, no experiments could be conducted in the hospital. Therefore, I could not spend the money.

Some committee members wanted me to name them as co-directors of my projects. They suggested that a protocol was more likely to be approved with the credibility of their names added to the research. We all knew it was a glorified bribe, as any co-director would have unrestricted access to the money. Even as I watched the value of the gift decrease with inflation, I refused to play the game. I earned a handsome living in private practice. I'd be damned if I was going to let anyone else feather his nest under the guise of "travel expenses" or bogus "honoraria."

Benford Harnett's generous gift sat in the hospital treasury for fifteen years. It rotted there because of pettiness and jealousy. No research ever benefited from his largesse.

Pettiness and Perfidy

During the 1950's and early 1960's, a diverse group of physicians made profound independent and consequential discoveries concerning heart attack. Dr. Bernard Lown at Harvard published extensively about the contributions of premature ventricular contraction (an extra heart beat) to ventricular fibrillation (a chaotic heart beat) and sudden death. Dr. Kouwenhoven at Johns Hopkins invented a relatively simple device to shock a heart with ventricular fibrillation back to a normal rhythm.

Unfortunately, it was rarely feasible to take advantage of these discoveries. Heart attack patients were generally assigned to random rooms all over the hospital, far removed from the nursing stations, so as to provide the patient with as much quiet and tranquility as possible. Regrettably, doing so prevented anyone from knowing what was happening to these patients in real time. Very often when we came to see a heart attack victim on morning rounds, we found the patient dead in bed.

The concept of the coronary care unit was developed by, among others, Dr. Hughes Day in Kansas City in the 1960s. Dr. Day pioneered the wild idea that if heart attacks were frequently associated with death, and the cause was most likely an unmonitored disturbance in cardiac rhythm, then congregating cardiac patients into one area of the hospital for constant and meticulous observation could lead to a reduced mortality. It took the coronary care unit to provide the forum in which patients who developed an abnormal heart rhythm could be diagnosed immediately, and expeditiously receive definitive therapy. It is remarkable (especially in hindsight) how the simplest ideas are often the most innovative.

St. Vincent's Chief of Medicine was Dr. Harold Winters. Dr. Winters was a gastroenterologist whose expertise was in psychosomatic illness. He published extensively on the subject. He had been recruited by St. Vincent's from Roosevelt Hospital. When he was awarded the title of Chief, he was given two mandates: recruit the best available medical students to the house staff, and recruit chiefs of departments who have a commitment to teaching.

St. Vincent's hospital was undergoing extensive modernization, constructing an entirely new building dedicated to medical research. Dr. Winters knew Dr. Day, and admired his innovation. He persuaded the hospital administration to create a coronary care unit in the new building, and although his field of expertise was far removed from his field of interest, the prerogative of office allowed him to name himself Chief of the new unit. Just like that, Dr. Winters became a cardiologist.

The unit opened in 1965 just as I began my year as Chief Resident. Since I had been the first Chief Resident in the coronary care unit, Dr. Winters invited me, a few years later, to co-author a book with him about our experience. I had no idea what was in store. I had to review the hospital records of every patient who entered the hospital with chest pain during the three years prior to the inception of the CCU. There were almost one thousand charts to process, which I tabulated evenings after dinner. Then, I reviewed the charts of the nearly six hundred patients with confirmed diagnoses of heart attack who were admitted to the CCU in the two years subsequent to its opening.

During that time, Dr. Nancy Neary, once a resident physician with me at St. Vincent's, returned from a fellowship in nephrology at Georgetown Medical School, where she had been studying under my former professor, Dr. George Schreiner. Back in 1959 Dr. Schreiner was the first to attempt repeated dialysis as a treatment for kidney failure. For thirty of the one hundred fifty six days that he was able to keep a young boy alive, I was on my pediatrics rotation, and was both witness to and participant in the experiment. It was a seminal event that proved a person with chronic kidney disease could, in fact, be kept alive indefinitely by externally cleansing his blood via a dialysis machine. The only reason the boy didn't live longer was because the repeated trauma to his arteries and veins from dialysis left him with no more access sites from which to draw blood. But with the invention of a silicone contraption by Dr. Scribner in Seattle, Washington, surgeons could construct a permanent vascular access point, and chronic dialysis became a feasible (and successful) treatment, for which Dr. Schreiner is credited for having spearheaded.

Dr. Neary returned from her fellowship and was immediately hired to be the director of a newly constituted department of nephrology. She needed help, and because I had experience with Dr. Schreiner and dialysis, I was invited to be her assistant. Nephrology and dialysis are far removed from cardiology, but it was an opportunity to learn and gain more experience. I certainly didn't accept the position for the money, as there was no stipend associated with the title "Associate Director," nor did Medicare or any private insurance carrier reimburse for dialysis.

The first year was uneventful. I made rounds with Nancy and helped her with dialysis as often as she needed me. I took weekend and evening calls to spell her, and our mutual respect grew. She taught me much about kidney disease, and the education compensated for the lack of a salary.

Meanwhile, I was still continuing my research in the CCU. While reviewing the patient records, I came upon a curious phenomenon. All the patients with proven heart attacks seemed to have a low level of oxygen in their blood, while those patients with chest pain from other causes had normal levels of oxygen. I shared this observation with Dr. Winters, who encouraged me to investigate it further.

To prove anything in medicine one needs objective, unbiased data. For months I arrived daily in the CCU at six o'clock in the morning to draw arterial blood on every patient admitted the previous day, before knowing the patient's ultimate diagnosis. Sampling blood from an artery is not difficult, but it is somewhat time consuming, uncomfortable for the patient, and, if not done properly, it can lead to serious complications. It is not as simple as drawing blood from a vein, but because venous blood has been depleted of oxygen by the organs of the body it serves, blood from an artery is required to measure how effective the lungs are in replacing the lost oxygen and how well the heart is pumping the blood.

Sure enough, once I tabulated the results and later correlated them with the final discharge diagnoses, every patient with a confirmed heart attack had low oxygen content, while the others had normal levels. The data was submitted for publication (with Dr. Winters as co-author), and it was accepted. The findings offered one of the early clues as to why heart attack victims suffer fatal rhythm disturbances: low oxygen causes the patient to breathe more rapidly to compensate, the rapid breathing necessarily blows off more carbon dioxide than normal, the lower level of carbon dioxide renders the blood slightly more alkaline, and it is this change in blood chemistry that is the proximate cause of rhythm disturbances.

Using the observations I made and the conclusions I reached, Dr. Winters invited the Chief Resident in Pulmonary Disease to perform a number of tests on several patients who had findings similar to the ones we published.

Together, they published a landmark paper in a prestigious medical journal. Conspicuous by its absence was my name among the authors. That omission should have been a wakeup call, but my naïveté knew no bounds. Instead, I watched as the paper received widespread acclaim, and Dr. Winters, as lead author, was confirmed as a pioneering cardiologist among his peers for all of his astute observations. He never again took care of a patient with a disease in gastroenterology.

As the reputation of the CCU that I helped to launch increased, my attendance at teaching rounds was requested less and less frequently, and by the end of the third year after it opened, I was no longer assigned to make rounds in the CCU at all. It was as if I no longer existed; I became a nonentity. I felt betrayed. The man I respected had cut me loose and allowed me to drift away from the pier that I helped to build, while he remained stable, on land, basking in the sunlight. Frankly, I resented it, but vengeance is not part of my nature. I reflected on one of my father's many aphorisms that he brought with him from the Middle East: Kill 'em with kindness. I said to myself, *Don't ever let him know how much your groin hurts from the kick he just gave you.*

Armed with all of the data I had been collecting from the CCU, Dr. Winters and I set out to write the book. In actuality, I wrote. Dr. Winters edited. The book was simply titled *The Coronary Care Unit.* When it was published in 1970, our hospital received enormous publicity. Dr. Winters went on the lecture circuit. We began to conduct seminars on how to set up and run a CCU. Physicians from all over the country came and paid medical homage to Dr. Winters, the innovator. Only once was I, as co-author, invited to lecture, and that was to a pitifully small hospital in northwestern Connecticut. It took all day to drive there and back, for which they paid no honorarium beyond gasoline reimbursement. I suspected that Dr. Winters gave me that assignment because he had better things to do that day.

I continued working with Nancy Neary. As awareness that something could be done for chronic kidney disease became more prevalent, many area hospitals found they lacked sufficient expertise to deliver specialized care. Beekman-Downtown Hospital had no one on its staff who knew anything about kidney disease. They needed someone to answer consultations, and they asked Dr. Winters to nominate someone. Dr. Neary was the logical choice, but she declined. She suggested that I do it, as she had neither the inclination nor the time. There was no additional compensation beyond fee for service. Still, it seemed like a perfectly fair arrangement to me, so I accepted the position.

A similar offer came from St. Clare's Hospital, but with somewhat different terms. In addition to my regular fee for service, St. Clare's would provide a stipend of five thousand dollars per annum as remuneration for delivering a weekly lecture in nephrology, making rounds with the house staff on all cases suspected of involving kidney disease, and making myself available for emergencies. It wasn't lavish compensation, but it was an attempt to recognize my contribution to teaching.

I accepted the appointment, but Dr. Winters insisted that the compensation be handled between the institutions. The money was to be paid to his department, which would then distribute a check to me. What he neglected to tell me was that I would only receive four thousand dollars per year. I never understood, nor was it ever explained, why he sequestered twenty dollars per week. Given our history together, I was already familiar with many of his quirks, but I thought it was too trivial a sum to make an issue of it, so I put up with the effrontery.

I was entering notes in a chart in the ICU at St. Clare's Hospital one day when the head nurse advised me that my wife was on the phone. Carol never called me while I was at work for anything other than lab reports. Concerned that something terrible had happened, I rushed to the phone. There was only a slight pause before Carol calmly announced, "You're going to be a father."

It had been five years since we married. Five years trying to conceive. Five years of doubt and frustration. Five years submitting to a laundry list of tests and fertility pills. Worst of all, five years of inane questions from family and friends, asking when we were planning to start a family. We had all but given up hope. And then, this phone call in the ICU happened, unexpectedly and without fanfare. I thought I would scream with joy, but standing in the middle of the unit, I thought the better of it and stifled my glee until I got home. Next to the day I walked Carol into the delivery suite and saw my son come into the world, it was the happiest day of my life.

His birth changed our lives. We had no idea how one little seven-pound bundle of energy could be so disrupting. The one bedroom apartment that had served us so well for five years immediately became cramped with paraphernalia. The bassinet, the baby carriage, the supplies all overwhelmed our little home. We had to move to larger quarters. We were conflicted, however, about where to go. Should we find a larger home in the city that we loved so well? Or would it be better to raise our child in suburban environs? Ultimately, we elected to leave the city, and eventually settled in a small town on the north shore of Long Island. It was only seventeen miles from New York, an eminently commutable distance either by railroad or automobile, and had a school system that was second to none. We found a house and settled in to a new life.

Even though the commute was relatively easy, it was still a commute, nonetheless. After leaving my wife and child at home to spend several weekends in the St. Clare's ICU dialyzing uninsured patients, knowing my fee would never be paid, I decided I had more right to those stupid extra twenty dollars each week than Dr. Winters ever had. It wasn't really about the money, nor was it about the time away from home. I was long accustomed to the long hours, and always believed that it was my duty to care for indigent patients. It was Winters's small-mindedness that irked me. I discussed the issue with the Chief of Medicine at St. Clare's, who was outraged. He immediately changed the terms of our agreement, and compensated me directly.

There is a curious thing about medicine. When there is no specialist available, doctors rarely makes a diagnosis relevant to that specialty. If they do make a diagnosis, they know nothing about how to treat it. As soon as a specialist appears on the scene, everyone becomes expert at identifying the symptoms relative to that specialty. In my case, I was the sole beneficiary when everyone at St. Clare's seemed to suddenly discover problems with kidneys. Physicians yearned to step forward to demonstrate their clinical acumen, and for awhile, I had more patients than I could handle. There were cases I might have attended, but could not. One can spread himself too thin.

On one of my tours with the house staff through the intensive care unit, I was asked to see a patient on the private surgical service. It was an irregular request, because I really had no right to be involved in the care of that individual, without an expressed request from the surgeon. I instructed the staff that my comments would be based only on the educational aspects of the case, and that my comments should in no way be construed as an official consultation.

The resident launched into his presentation. It was simple and straightforward. A middle-aged woman presented with a bleeding peptic ulcer. After ten units of transfused blood, she continued to hemorrhage, and her blood pressure remained unstable. The surgeon elected to operate on her to remove two-thirds of her stomach, a time-honored procedure in the decades before Zantac, Pepcid, and myriad other histamine antagonists. Unfortunately, the combination of hemorrhage, unstable blood pressure, multiple transfusions, and the stress of major surgery caused the patient's kidneys to fail postoperatively.

This set of circumstances was not uncommon. The patient was making no urine and she was becoming uremic. I suggested that the patient undergo dialysis; otherwise, she would likely die. As we finished, one of the members of the house staff pulled me aside to tell me that they all had already come to the same conclusion, and agreed with my conviction, but had invited me to discuss the case so that I might persuade the attending physician to recommend the procedure. The attending physician in this case was none other that the Chief of Surgery.

Dr. John McManus was an icon at St. Clare's Hospital, his reputation legendary. He admitted so many patients that he virtually dictated policy to the nuns as to how the hospital would be run. He held absolute control over the operating rooms' schedule, and he parceled time like rations in a concentration camp. Any physician who failed to heel to his command soon found himself without time in the operating suite. Moreover, if another surgeon had a patient whose disease entity interested him, McManus would take over the case. While there was no doubt that he was one of the most accomplished general surgeons in New York, there was also little doubt that John McManus's arrogance rivaled his ego.

The next morning, I chanced to meet him in the ICU. I was writing a note in a chart when he entered the room, an entourage of physicians following close behind. He wore a meticulously tailored suit that could easily have been in the window of Brooks Brothers. He moved from patient to patient on the surgical side, lingering at each bedside while a resident physician brought him up to date, whereupon he dictated orders or treatment he wished to be implemented, and moved on to the next bed. When he reached the desk where I was writing, he commented, "I understand you've been seeing my patient."

"Yes sir," I replied, "but only in an educational forum."

"I understand you think she should have dialysis."

"Yes, Dr. McManus. Her blood urea is over one fifty, and her potassium is skirting dangerously high levels. She's making virtually no urine." Her blood urea was nearly ten times the normal levels, and her potassium levels threatened to stop her heart. "It's most unlikely that she'll come out of profound renal failure on her own," I continued. "It is my opinion she will die, unless she undergoes dialysis."

"Hmm," he mused. "I've considered starting up a dialysis unit under the aegis of the department of surgery. Would you be willing to run it?"

The request was stunning. He hardly knew me. We'd never before met. Why would he make such an offer? Perhaps the scuttlebutt had reached his ears that the house staff was learning something from my weekly lectures. Perhaps the attending physicians whose patients benefited from dialysis spoke up at meeting about my dedication.

The larger issue was his proposal to establish a *medical* discipline within his own *surgical* department. His hubris flew in the face of accepted medical standards.

"I'm truly flattered," I replied, "but I must decline. Dialysis is a medical discipline. Nowhere is it run by surgeons."

He coughed. He took a handkerchief from the breast pocket of his jacket and rubbed his nose, folded the handkerchief carefully, and replaced it. He lingered for a moment, looking at nothing in particular, turned, and walked away with the mob swarming close behind.

My recommendation to dialyze the patient went unilaterally ignored. It would have required that the patient be transferred to St. Vincent's, as her recent abdominal surgery precluded peritoneal dialysis, and St. Clare's had neither the equipment nor the personnel to run hemodialysis. The patient was never dialyzed, and no one from the medical service was officially called in consultation. She died two days later. The only mercy is that she slipped into a painless uremic coma.

In all the years I have been associated with the practice of medicine, I have never met anyone more despicable than John McManus. He was a despotic egotist with an utter disregard for human life. Not one physician, surgeon, or administrator rebuked him or confronted him. He held too much sway. He may have had an enormous practice and may have been revered as a surgical giant. I knew that he was an egomaniacal murderer. I never regretted not working for him.

I continued shuttling among three hospitals, answering consults and addressing weekend emergencies. I became a regular at the Brittany de Soir, a lovely French restaurant located at the corner of Ninth Avenue and Fifty-First Street, across the street from St. Clare's. They had a superb menu and modest prices. The waitresses, with their French accents and measured indifference, knew me well, as I often dined there on Fridays and Saturdays while I supervised peritoneal dialysis across the street. Clinical problems that germinated during the week always seemed to grow into disasters by Friday afternoon, leading to the inevitable emergency consultation on Friday night. No physician wanted a weekend death on his hands. It was preferable to call in the consult and let me wrestle with the problem, so the physician of record could keep his appointment at the theatre.

During my years as an itinerant consultant, the patients who were too sick to be dialyzed at the outlying hospitals were transferred to St. Vincent's. This flattered Administration's perception of being a medical center, and it helped to maintain the census at the hospital. Unfortunately, it threatened Dr. Neary's ego.

As the years progressed, acute and chronic dialysis eventually came under the purview of Medicare. The reimbursement was generous. Taken on its own, the Medicare reimbursement was downright extravagant, until one recalls how long we had dialyzed patients without any compensation at all. Whereas the harder I worked, the more I stood to earn, Dr. Neary had no inclination to expand her practice or dialysis program, because her employment contract called for her to return to the hospital any income earned over and above her salary. Money was therefore no incentive for her, and neither, regrettably, was treating the wretches of society who could have benefitted from her expertise. Extra work was uncompensated, so she simply declined to do it, with the excuse that she was too busy with academic work. She chose instead to study and treat a few select patients with exotic diseases, then write papers and publish them in the medical literature. She believed that doing so would solidify her status among her peers, and entrench her in her position as Chief of Nephrology.

It was quite clear that I was earning more money than Dr. Neary. One only had to count the number of patients in my care. But I saw no reason to restrict my own practice merely because she had elected to work for the hospital as a salaried employee. But with increasing frequency, I found that my patients were being denied access to the dialysis unit on the ruse that I was taxing the capacity of the staff. My suggestion that she hire more staff was met with rebuke.

She demanded a meeting with the Chief of Medicine. I was glad to have an intermediary. Believing he would arbitrate our differences, we at last had a confrontation in Dr. Winter's office.

He's bringing too many patients to my unit," she complained.

"Your unit?" I challenged.

"I am responsible for every patient undergoing dialysis."

"Bullshit, Nancy! You're pissed because I'm busier than you."

"I simply do not have the staff to accommodate him," she implored Dr. Winters.

"Then hire more staff!" I reasoned.

"Why should I hire more staff just so you can make more money?"

"Jesus, Nancy, I am not going to apologize for making money. What would you have me do? Let them all die because you don't want to get off your ass?"

The donnybrook lasted only a short time before Nancy stormed out of the office, uttering threats and epithets. Throughout it all, Dr. Winters said nothing. He sat mute in his swivel chair. He took no side and resolved no issue, so for as long as she remained Chief, I had to kiss Nancy Neary's ass every time I needed to get a sick, dying patient transferred to my hospital for dialysis.

Several years later, Nancy made one demand too many, and threatened to resign if her requests were not met. Dr. Winters finally hitched up his jock and accepted her resignation. I was not sad to see her go.

Carol and I had settled into our life in suburbia, and we enjoyed hosting dinner parties in our home. It's a Middle East tradition and part of my DNA. Being Italian, Carol shared a similar Mediterranean culture and commitment to hospitality. While she did not particularly enjoy daily cooking, she reveled in dining, and for our parties she dug deep into her heritage, marshaled her genes, and cooked sumptuous feasts. She'd assemble a vast antipasto. The buffet tables would be set for royalty. She'd make stuffed hams and roast beef, accompanied by saffron rice with toasted pignoli nuts. Whipped sweet potatoes topped with marshmallow and several salads, from red cabbage to string beans with artichoke hearts and water chestnuts, rounded out the main course. For dessert, even the simplest Jell-O mold with fruit taxed everyone's ability to eat it.

We earmarked one of these festive parties for our professional colleagues. It had been quite some time since we entertained physicians in our home, and having had accepted many dinner invitations, we felt obliged to reciprocate. As fate would have it, we were now neighbors with Dr. Winters. Both Carol and I felt that hatchets were better left buried. We were doing well. My practice was booming. Best of all, I had a son after a five-year marathon trying for conception. The future could not have been brighter. We extended an invitation. He accepted.

The evening was typical for a doctors' party. The conversation centered on hospital nonsense, pontificating, and puffery. There was not one sentence uttered with respect to current events. There was no banter, no flirtation, no discussion of culture, entertainment, or the most recent Broadway play. It was, to say the least, a boring party. Thank goodness there was an ample supply of good California wine. I think I drank almost a liter by myself, just to get through the evening. As I entered the kitchen to open yet another bottle, I found my wife in the midst of preparing dessert. She looked at me, with a long-suffering, weary gaze in her eye, and remarked, "My God, the minute hand on the clock is moving so damn slowly!" We spontaneously convulsed with laughter, trying fruitlessly to stifle our mirth, lest someone should overhear.

At last, our guests departed, led by Dr. Winters—who profusely thanked my wife for a sumptuous meal and me for the selection of wine— and by Monday morning, we all plunged back into our respective roles and responsibilities.

The reputation of St. Vincent's hospital was on the rise in the early 1970s. It may have been spearheaded by the coronary care unit, but other innovations were taking place. In addition to the dialysis unit, a state of the art cardiac catheterization laboratory was built. The open-heart coronary bypass surgical program was accelerating at breathtaking speed. A neonatal ICU was constructed, and interventional radiology was pioneered. With all its success, the hospital administration began to look to other hospitals as a resource for patient referrals. There was a rumor that St. Vincent's was considering a merger with Beekman-Downtown Hospital.

Illness never strikes at an opportune time. It was no exception for Dr. Winters. He had commenced a new exercise program, and everyone attributed his rapid weight loss to the vigor of that program. However, when he began to look gaunt and run erratic fever, the suspicions grew. Soon after, the diagnosis of a malignancy was made; he had a rare, aggressive, and fatal tumor. The precipitous course of his illness dictated a hasty transition of power and responsibilities, but within three months of his diagnosis, Dr. Winters was dead.

The merger with Beekman-Downtown moved forward. Uncertainty prevailed in our institution. Dr. Winters had named a friend of mine, a former classmate, to chair the liaison committee between the two hospitals. Among other things, it was his responsibility to recruit and name the new chiefs of departments. The Chief of Medicine at Beekman-Downtown appreciated the effort I had expended at his hospital, and initiated correspondence to nominate me for chief of the nephrology department. Having spent several years as the only doctor attending to patients in renal failure, I felt that it was a foregone conclusion that the position was mine. To my utter shock and dismay, I was not appointed. I stormed into my friend's office.

"What is this bullshit?" I shouted. "Why am I being passed over?"

"I'm sorry, Vic..." Jason began.

"I don't want to hear from 'I'm sorry!' I'm the only guy busting my ass at Beekman. I've been doing it for years with no one else's help, for no compensation, and after all my dedication, my years of service, my hard work, you have no right to give it to anyone else!"

I continued to scream at him until I ran out of air.

"Vic," my so-called friend whispered in the brief pause of my tirade, "Winters disqualified you from consideration. He said you didn't need the position. He thought you were doing well enough in private practice and didn't need the money."

I stared at him, incredulously.

"With that logic," I seethed, "You should select the dumbest fucking moron you can find, so long as he is destitute! Winters is dead, Jason, how can you sit there and continue to follow insane directives from the grave?"

I turned and stormed out of his office.

That son of a bitch, I screamed to myself. *He came to my home, ate my food and drank my wine, and all the while, he was taking inventory. The jealous little bastard was counting my money. He deprived me of a just reward, not for lack of merit, but for pettiness.*

James

The ride home on the Long Island Expressway was more tedious than usual. Traffic was at a standstill. A cacophony of thoughts echoed in my mind. Ideas, images, and feelings ricocheted and darted into a maddening blur. Traffic slowed inversely to the frenzy of my mental kaleidoscope. Rain pelted the windshield and I absently turned on the wipers. My exit appeared, and I turned off the highway to negotiate the glistening pavement of the side streets. At last, I found my driveway. The silence that enveloped me when I turned off the engine was deafening.

I had endured many frustrations as a doctor, but today's failure eclipsed all of the trials and defeats I had experienced in my twenty years of being a physician. There was no way to share with anyone the emptiness I was feeling, so I did not try. My wife silently observed my entrance. She watched as I poured a lot of vodka over some ice, and slowly drank it, each sip causing another tear to well up in my eyes. Carol softly touched my shoulder. We both began to weep. We held each other tightly, and the sobs came, uncontrollably. Finally I spoke.

"He didn't stand a chance."

"You did all that you could."

"Tell that to Vera."

In the years since we moved to our new community, Carol had become very close friends with Vera Schroff. They met at a bridge party and bonded immediately. They visited each other for coffee and would talk for hours about everything and nothing at once. Vera's husband, Eddie, marketed and sold oil tanks. He and I ran in completely different circles, but when we got together, we found we had much in common, having been brought up similarly. He had a particularly gruff personality, but it was all a polished facade.

All one needed to do was to confront him. He would laugh and transform into the sweetest guy imaginable and tell a stupid joke.

Vera and Eddie's son James had congenital heart disease. James was slight of build, and he had a shaggy, mop-top head of hair that only partially covered his rather large ears. His skin was pale, almost white, and he wore large-framed tinted glasses. He walked with a hint of a sway-backed swagger, and might have looked like a member of a 70s rock band, if not for his deep blue lips and clubbed fingers, both results of the abnormal blood flow within his disfigured heart. He had a highly arched palate, which gave his voice a peculiarly hollow tone. And, if that weren't enough, he was cursed with a morbid form of pustular acne.

He was difficult to look at. It was not the acne, not the blue lips, not the voice, not the face. No, it was death itself. We adults knew we were seeing a boy who would soon die, and looking into the face of death forced us to struggle with our own mortality.

But James had a resignation and strength of character that grew out of that fear, because he had already conquered it. He knew from the moment he could understand universal truth that he would die before his time. It was this understanding, I believe, that enabled him to be empathetic to so many other kids. Despite his ailments and his physical appearance, James was friend to a large group of somewhat troubled teens in our community. I marveled at how kids would seek out his company to pour out their hearts to this dying young guru with the blue lips. Those with drug problems or school problems or parental problems or girl problems sought him out. James was a friend to them all. He would entertain them on his guitar or piano. (He had long given up on wind instruments and drums, but I was told that when he was less ill he played several instruments very well.) Teenagers spent endless hours in the basement of his home, sitting around and listening to music. In the summertime, he'd walk along the side streets, hand in hand with the prettiest girls. James would hear their confessions and listen to their fears. No one was afraid to tell James anything; he had faced the ultimate fear and had overcome it.

That same resignation that seemed so effortless for James came much harder for the rest of the Schroff family. No one could love his "Jamesie" more than Ed, and he long lived with the hope that James would somehow be cured. But the reality of the situation became clearer and clearer with each successive complication, and Eddie ultimately quit his job so that he could care for James full-time.

One day, out of the clear blue, Vera and Eddie asked me if I would take care of James, be his doctor. I knew when they asked that they were no longer searching for cures. They were looking for a doctor who would responsibly care for their son in his final years. I knew firsthand how illness could destroy a family, having a sister who suffered with combined scoliosis and polio, another sister who had a nervous breakdown, and a brother who stuttered horribly. I accepted the Schroff's request because I believed I could provide some measure of stability and comfort. We all knew intuitively there was no long-term plan.

The Schroff's resignation grew when James' heart occupied the full breadth of his chest, squeezing away his lungs so that he could barely breathe; when his liver and spleen enlarged to occupy most of his abdominal cavity so he could no longer eat; when he became so emaciated that he could no longer walk to the bathroom unescorted. He slept most of the day, awakening only to take a few sips of liquid and be reassured by his parents continued vigil, a vigil that had lasted for nineteen years and was now constant in the final days of his life. He became jaundiced. The whites of his eyes turned deep yellow, in garish contrast to the blue of his lips. Nature was cruel.

James eventually became so profoundly weak that we all felt that he might be made more comfortable if he were in the hospital. Vera and Ed were exhausted, and I felt that hospitalization would relieve them of some of the everyday stresses so they could get some rest.

James had no sooner occupied his hospital bed than the macabre dance began. St. Vincent's was a teaching hospital, so interns and residents flocked to the bedside to listen to strange murmurs. The cardiology fellow was called in consultation to see this "interesting case." The next morning, I was assaulted by an army of house staff asking—no, demanding—to perform tests to uncover the source of James' problems. They were not tempered by the assurance I gave that he had already undergone surgery three times by the most eminent cardiac surgeons in America, and that none were successful. The new logic of the modern hospital demanded that every study, no matter how redundant, had to be performed, lest some inconsequential reversible problem be discovered.

There were official and unofficial consultations with a number of cardiologists and with the Chief of Cardiology, the Director of Medicine, a gastroenterologist, a psychologist, and a minister. All were eager to lend advice. James dismissed the minister, refusing to see him. He had no use for religiosity. The house staff would listen to a consultant, and like the Pied

Piper, dutifully follow him off to conference, only to do an about-face at the words of the next consultant.

James' jaundice was extreme. All the consultants believed he had an obstruction in his bile duct, and if that were the case, removal of the stone would offer him relief. The recent successes in medicine and surgery had led to a new wave of education that suggested that every malady could be cured. They could not accept that his jaundice was the result of profound, unrelenting, chronic heart failure alone. The responsibility for action, however, was mine. While everyone was free with advice, James was my patient, and the decision to act—or not to act—was mine alone.

House staff badgered me. *How can you let a teenager die without doing everything to save him!*

I wanted to say that everything that reasonably could have been done for James had been done, but how and when does one make that determination? What is the definition of reasonable? James had been in and out of hospitals all his life. He'd already had three failed open-heart surgeries. When is it appropriate for us to admit defeat? For centuries, it was considered good medical care for physicians to merely be a comforting presence at the bedside, without having to apologize for the failure of the latest contraption, or medicine, or procedure, or intervention. I could either subscribe to that time-honored tradition, and do nothing but render comfort until James' impending demise, or I could intervene, cure nothing and maybe prolong his life a little—for a day, perhaps for months, but certainly not for years. Then again, any intervention could accelerate death. No choice was clear, but one had to be made.

Primum non nocere; first, do no harm. It rang in my ears like an echoing gong. My heart and my gut told me to do nothing.

Instead, I succumbed to the folly. James was wheeled to the diagnostic lab to undergo a test to determine if there was an obstruction to the flow of bile. He was administered a sedative and an analgesic before an endoscope was introduced through the mouth into the stomach, past the pylorus into the duodenum, where the common bile duct was infused with a contrast agent that detailed the architecture of the liver on X-ray. There was no obstructing lesion. There was no curable disease. There was nothing to be done.

The anesthetic and analgesic, however, were more than James' liver could metabolize. He never woke up.

The blue-lipped teenager and the corpse I pronounced dead were one and the same. For nineteen years his mother anticipated this day, while his father tried to believe that it would never happen. The endless examinations, the unrequited hope of open-heart surgeries, the special schools, the tutoring, the guilt, the grief, the recriminations, the accusations, the resignation, the lonely nights, the separation from friends, the anger, all had culminated in today's final loss.

The tears Carol and I shed on the night of James' death continued. I asked myself how I could have been so vulnerable to the whims of my house staff. How could I have lost my perspective, ignored my instincts? Did thirty years of medical education and practice teach me anything?

There are no easy answers. There are only difficult choices.

Carol

During the 1950s, when I was still in medical school, Dr. Irving Cooper at Columbia University experimented in Parkinson's research by inserting a probe into a specific area of the brain, and either freezing it or injecting it with alcohol. By destroying small cellular structures, he was able to improve the functionality of many patients with Parkinson's disease. Unfortunately, there were no advanced imaging technologies in his day, so his was essentially a blind procedure, relying solely on visible anatomic landmarks. Many of his patients suffered irreparable damage, and he was largely vilified for his complication rate.

By the mid 1980s, a mere thirty years later, breakthroughs in digital imaging and electronic mapping of the brain made it possible to insert a probe to an exact location the size of a pea. I had read reports in the medical literature of experimental trials in which patients with Parkinson's disease benefited from a new procedure called Deep Brain Stimulation. The surgery was pioneered by Dr. Alim Benebid in Grenoble, France. He and his colleagues discovered that brain tissue need not be destroyed to derive benefit. Rather, by transmitting a minuscule electric current in the subthalamic nucleus, they were able to interrupt abnormal cellular transmission and restore near normal function to an afflicted patient. It took little time before neurosurgeons in the United States petitioned the FDA to allow them to follow in Dr. Benebid's footsteps.

The results of the American trials were promising and exciting. We looked at DBS research programs in Atlanta, New York, Boston, and Toronto. Atlanta was at the forefront, but getting into their program was difficult, because there were already many patients on their waiting list. The New York program was likewise full.

"Well, Carol, would you rather go to Boston or Toronto?"

"Let's go to Toronto, and make a vacation out of it."

"I like the way you think."

We scheduled an appointment, and boarded a small jet plane for the short trip across the border. As we flew north, I recalled my patient with acromegaly, Edna, who I sent to Montreal for treatment. I remembered the cure she found by following innovative medicine wherever it required she go. Her life was saved. Now it was I taking my own advice, travelling to the cutting edge, hoping for a miracle for Carol.

We arrived at Toronto General Hospital the morning after we landed. We were greeted cordially by the hospital receptionist, and led to the neurosurgical wing. Four members of the Toronto team examined Carol independently. At the conclusion of their examinations, the Chief of Neurosurgery,

Dr. Thorndyke, brought us into his office and had us sit with him at a small conference table. He looked at Carol squarely and said, "You are a good candidate for the procedure. We'd be happy to do it here."

"When would you schedule it?" I asked.

"Right away, if you want. We could begin the pre-operative assessment within the next two weeks."

We were somewhat taken aback, surprised mostly, by their ability to schedule such a profound operation so quickly. We thanked him, and told him we needed to talk it over.

"I understand," Dr. Thorndyke said. He shook Carol's hand. "Whenever you are ready. We'll be here."

That night in our hotel room, we discussed the advice. It was strange to us that there seemed so few patients taking part in the protocol, especially given the demand and wait lists we had encountered at the other research centers.

"They were so eager to get started," Carol mused.

"Well, that's to be expected. It's new medicine. They're excited."

"A little too eager," she added, exaggeratedly wringing her hands and making a face like a mad scientist.

"Oh, come on now," I giggled, "They had your best interests at heart."

"I know. But I still would like another opinion."

We traveled to Boston, Massachusetts. The team was quite professional. Carol received an evaluation similar to the one in Toronto. A neurologist spent the better part of two hours taking a detailed history and performing a neurological examination. At its conclusion, we were brought in to meet with the Chief of Neurosurgery, Dr. Royce Coughlin. He was a tall and exceptionally handsome man, and it seemed to me that Carol got just a little weaker in the knees than usual when she spoke with him.

Dr. Coughlin reviewed the report from the neurologist, turned to Carol and said, "You definitely qualify for the Deep Brain procedure."

Carol asked him, "When would you do it?"

"When you are desperate," he said simply.

It was the most honest answer I had heard.

The Boston team ranked high on our list as we continued to try to meet with the other research centers. We were in communication with the team in Atlanta, Georgia, but they ultimately told us that it would be many months before they could schedule us for an initial evaluation. It was a daunting timeframe, considering we had already met with two highly qualified and accommodating teams elsewhere.

At about the same time as we decided to abandon Atlanta, we learned that New York University Hospital was in the process of recruiting new patients for their program. We called for an appointment, and to our pleasant surprise, learned that the Chief of Neurosurgery, himself, would make the initial evaluation.

Dr. Sean McCarthy was kind and affable, and he had an engaging personality. After a thorough exam, he said he'd be happy to accept Carol into his program. We were taken by his candor.

"You do realize, Carol, that the operation is considered experimental by the FDA?"

Carol nodded, "Yes, I'm well aware."

"So you understand that there is a protocol that we must follow. Everything we do we do in an attempt to convince the FDA to approve the procedure. There will be a lot of tests and exercises, and there will be a lot of documentation. You'll have to be examined and approved by a number of different physicians before we can move forward with the surgery."

Carol and I both nodded in assent.

"And I also must mention that, because it's experimental, Medicare will not pay for any of it. You'll have to pay out of pocket."

"Yes, we know," I said.

"I'm sorry to have to be so blunt."

"No, believe me, I understand," I said. "Nobody expects you to do this for free!"

"You'd be surprised!" Dr. McCarthy chuckled. He looked at Carol and gave her an affable wink, and continued, "Now, there are a few things you should know about the procedure. First of all, it's a two-day affair."

"Two days?" Carol's eyes got wide.

"The first day is minor intake business. In the evening, we'll get you set up with a stereotactic frame."

"What is that?"

"We commonly call it a 'halo,' because that's what it looks like. It's a device that is attached directly to the skull. It's used to keep your head completely immobilized during surgery, and we use it to calibrate where to insert the probes. It's a quick procedure, but you will have to wear the halo overnight."

"OK."

"The next day will be a marathon. There's no other way of saying it. In the morning, we'll take you for an MRI of your head, with the halo attached. Once we get those films from Radiology, we will take you to the surgical suite and get started. We only make two small holes in the front of your skull," Dr. McCarthy said, pointing with his index and middle fingers to an area just above his own hairline, "through which we insert the probes. You'll have some local anesthesia, but you have to know that we will need you to be conscious for the majority of the surgery to know that the probes are properly placed."

I could see Carol swallow hard before asking, "How long will that take?"

"Honestly? Six to eight hours."

Carol looked to me, and I could see in her expression a distinct fear that she would not be able to endure the lengthy procedure. Her back surgery had mitigated the pain she experienced whenever she lie prone, but it hadn't eliminated it, and she was still suffering occasional discomfort.

"Once we have the probes set, we remove the halo and tunnel the wires under your scalp and into your chest cavity, where we attach them to two neurostimulators that we implant in your chest like pacemakers."

"Will I be awake for that, too?" Carol asked.

"Oh, no, no, no. Of course not. By that point, you've earned the right to sleep, don't you think?"

"I should hope so!" Carol smiled a nervous smile.

"All in all, it will likely be a ten-hour surgery. We'll send you home for about two weeks or so, to rest and recuperate. Then we'll bring you back in, and one of my colleagues will turn the stimulators on. And that should be that!" He smiled. "Do you have any questions for me?"

"No, I don't think so." Carol looked overwhelmed, but satisfied.

"Good. Then we can begin the evaluations. My secretary will provide a list of physicians for you so you can begin to make the appointments."

We had three viable teams from which to choose. Each institution prescribed specific requirements for patients to satisfy their experimental protocol, but all required that Carol be evaluated by countless doctors in varying disciplines. Because it would take several months to accomplish all the tasks that were required, we ultimately elected to go with the nearby NYU team, rather than travel repeatedly to a distant location.

The first doctor on our list was Dr. Boris Stancic, the neurologist who headed the Parkinson's program out of Beth Israel Hospital, an affiliate of NYU. He was the most humane man I have ever met. He treated Carol with exceptional kindness. Over the course of several visits, he videotaped Carol performing various tasks: touching each finger to her thumb, repeatedly lifting her leg from a seated position, walking unescorted down a hallway.

Carol then had to return for several more visits to repeat the tasks, this time without having taken any of her Parkinson's medication. In Carol's case, the differences were negligible, because she was taking practically no Sinemet anymore, but she went through the exercises faithfully.

We were sent to Mount Sinai Hospital for a study of her nervous system function. Mount Sinai is not a part of the New York University Hospital network, but apparently, this neurophysiologist was the only one regionally qualified to perform the tests required for Deep Brain Stimulation research. Over the course of several sessions together, he took dutiful notes as he observed Carol performing various exercises to the point of fatigue. He was more a technician than a doctor, and he never made an effort to establish a relationship with us, with the one glaring exception when he suggested that we abandon the New York University program to join his program at Mount Sinai. He was most disagreeable when we declined.

"We have just as good a program as NYU," he boasted.

"I'm certain you do, but we have already established a relationship with Dr. McCarthy."

"Fine," he harrumphed, and he stood up and walked out of the room.

Carol had to undergo a PET scan, a sophisticated imaging technique that highlights functional processes in the body. At the time, the only machine available in the New York metropolitan area was at North Shore Hospital, a mere three miles from our home. A radioactive "tracer" that is preferentially taken up by the brain was injected into Carol's arm, and a scan of her head was taken. The resulting image confirmed that not only did she have Parkinson's disease, but it ruled out any other condition that could conceivably be the cause of her tremor.

Carol was sent to a neuropsychologist, an expert in discerning how anatomic or physiologic abnormalities impact behavior. In an effort to determine if and how Carol's Parkinson's disease affected her personality, he asked her uncountable questions of all manner and stripe. Carol sat with him for hours.

"How'd it go?" I asked, as I wheeled her to the car.

"Vic, it was the verbal equivalent of a Rorschach test. The questions were more like an intelligence exam than anything else."

"Why? What questions did he ask you?"

"Who could remember? There were so many!"

Later, a psychiatrist evaluated Carol to determine if she understood the magnitude of the surgery she was about to undertake. It was a perfunctory visit. The brevity of it led me to believe that is was meant only to cover all the bases to further insulate the research team from any liability beyond the waivers we had already signed prior to seeing any of the doctors.

At last, she had to be evaluated by an internist to insure she would survive the surgery. She was otherwise perfectly healthy, but in the intervening year since the laminectomy, Carol's back had deteriorated. The pain had by now returned as bad as it ever had been before. There was no way she'd be able to remain still on the operating table. Dr. McCarthy suggested that she be reevaluated, and perhaps consider undergoing another back surgery.

"Go see Dr. Cramer on our staff," he said. "He's an excellent surgeon, and I have the utmost confidence in his opinion."

I sat with Carol in Dr. Cramer's office as Carol detailed her problem.

"About a year ago, I had a laminectomy at North Shore. The surgery helped, for sure, but the pain has since gotten worse, to the point where I am back to where I was pre-surgery," Carol explained. "I don't know what happened, because I followed Dr. Rosenfeld's instructions and wore the back brace religiously, but I was never completely free from pain."

"A back brace?" Dr. Cramer asked with a look of incredulity.

"Yes, she had me fitted with a custom back brace to wear post-surgery."

"A custom back brace? Who made the brace?" Dr. Cramer looked alternately to Carol and myself for an answer.

"Haverstraw Orthotics," I interjected.

"Ah," he said with a knowing smirk.

"What do you mean, 'Ah?'" I asked.

"Oh, nothing. It's just that Rosenfeld's brother-in-law owns Haverstraw Orthotics."

"Nepotism has many faces, doesn't it?" I said, as Carol rolled her eyes.

Dr. Cramer sent Carol for a new round of X-rays, which confirmed that the original surgery was incomplete. Carol underwent a second laminectomy at NYU that went smoothly. No corset-like contraption was involved.

Carol was discharged on the second post-operative day and I took her home to convalesce. For the first time in her adult life, she was completely free of back pain. Three weeks after surgery, as she was taking her seat at the dinner table, Carol gasped and winced and clutched the table's edge.

"Honey, what wrong?" I asked, alarmed.

"I don't know. I just got a horrible stabbing pain in my back." She breathed a heavy sigh as she lowered herself into her chair.

Over the course of the next couple of weeks, the pain continued, catching her at odd times during the day, and completely taking her breath away with its intensity. We returned to see the surgeon, and after another round of MRIs, C-T scans and myelograms, Dr. Cramer announced that she had developed a synovial cyst at her surgical site, and that it was pressing on the nerves in her spine. The cure was yet more surgery on her back.

We arrived at the hospital at six o'clock in the morning for scheduled surgery at eight. I helped Carol into her hospital gown, and sat with her in her room. A nurse breezed in and administered pre-operative medication. As the sedation began to take effect, Carol turned to me and said, "I feel like a character in a Kafka novel,"

There was an element of truth to her comment. "What about me?" I pleaded.

"Oh, you're just a minor character. I'm the main event," she softly slurred.

The next morning, Dr. Cramer came to make rounds. He inspected the surgical wound, performed several reflex tests, then motioned to me to meet him in the hall. I had a sinking feeling he was about to deliver awful news. He put his arm on my shoulder and said, "You know as well as I that hospitals are notorious for transmitting infections."

"I hear you loud and clear," I replied, relieved. Within the hour I was wheeling Carol to our car to take her home to convalesce there.

Brain surgery was finally scheduled for early December. Knowing that Carol would be in the hospital for a number of days, and knowing what a saga it would be for both of us, I decided to take a room at a nearby hotel. I didn't want to have to worry about traffic in and out of the city, and I didn't want Carol's first day to start any earlier than it absolutely had to.

We arrived at Dr. McCarthy's office suite in the hospital first thing the next morning, and I dutifully handed his secretary a cashier's check for a very large sum of money. She took it from me, and fastidiously went about ensuring its validity. Once she was certain it was the real thing, and once it had been tucked safely away, she looked up cheerily at us and said, "Welcome! We're so glad you're here. Let's get you settled."

Carol was admitted to the hospital, and late that afternoon her head was shaved clean and the halo was secured to her skull with screws. Inscribed with markings to indicate the full three hundred sixty degrees of its arc, the halo was a heavy, two-inch circle of metal that wrapped completely around her head just above her eyebrows. From ear to ear, another arc of similarly calibrated metal curved over the top of her head.

"It's bad enough trying to get any sleep in these places without this contraption clamped to my head," Carol fumed when I came in to see her. "I'm going to be up all night!"

At six o'clock the next morning she was brought to the radiology suite to have the MRI taken of her head with the halo in place. I came to visit her at noon—long after the MRI should have been completed and shortly before she would go into surgery—to find her room empty. When I inquired as to her whereabouts, I was informed that she was still in the X-ray department. I wended my way through the maze of the hospital to find Carol lying alone on a gurney in an alcove with no one in attendance. She was scrunched up, lying on her side, uncovered and unable to move because of the weight of the halo anchored to her head.

"Carol! What are you doing here?" I asked, stupidly.

"I don't know. They left me here hours ago."

I was immediately filled with a visceral rage, but I knew never to get on the wrong side of hospital personnel. I forced myself to regain my composure, and found a nurse whom I asked with all the control I had to help me get my wife into a comfortable position and back to her room.

Within minutes of getting settled again, a nurse and an orderly arrived to take her back to the X-ray department.

"Why is she going back to X-Ray?" I asked.

"She's scheduled for an MRI," the orderly said.

"But I had the MRI this morning," Carol said, looking to the nurse. "Shouldn't I be going to surgery now?"

"We're sorry, Mrs. Keyloun," the nurse began, matter-of-factly, "but we have to do the MRI over again. It seems someone pushed a wrong button, and the data from your original scan has been lost."

"Oh," Carol whispered, defeated. She turned to me and said, "They lost my MRI? Is that normal?"

"Yeah, yeah, it happens, honey. They'll just do it over again." I tried to downplay the egregiousness of the oversight, but inside my blood was boiling.

No sooner had the gurney rounded the door of her room into the hall then Carol suffered a panic attack. She began screaming and crying, writhing and clutching the rails at the side of her gurney. The orderly stopped, and looked around, flustered. Nurses came running from their stations to try to settle the commotion. I helped Carol to sit up, and we all tried talking her down. Happily, it had been recorded in her chart that she was susceptible to panic attacks, and in short order someone arrived with Atavan and some water. Carol finally settled, lay back down, and went off to repeat the MRI all over again.

It wasn't until sometime around four o'clock that afternoon that Carol was finally given something to eat. About the same time that her food arrived (essentially her breakfast), a member of the surgical team came in to the room to inform us that it was too late in the day to begin the DBS procedure. The surgery that was scheduled to follow the MRI had to be postponed until the next morning, and Carol had to spend another night with the halo affixed to her head.

That next day was the longest I can remember. Carol's surgery began at seven o'clock in the morning. I had been reminded again that surgery would last at least ten hours. Even with the halo and the MRI, it would take many hours to locate the precise area where the electronic probes should be inserted. Once they were secured, it would take many more hours still to tunnel wires under the skin of her scalp, neck and chest to the place where the neurostimulators would be inserted under her collarbone. I arrived at the hospital at noon. Our son arrived at the hospital a little while later, and we waited together for news of Carol's progress. Finally, Dr. McCarthy's nurse approached us with news that it was all going terrifically well.

"Both probes have been implanted and secured," she told us gleefully. The nervous waiting had me and my son exhausted, but we were happy for the update. "It took them a little longer than they expected to implant the first probe. Apparently, they couldn't pinpoint the right spot." I liked her. She was energized by the science, she was genuinely excited for us, and she was always honest with us. "But once they set the first probe, the second one went in very easily." She offered me an X-ray jacket, "Here, Dr. McCarthy thought this might interest you. It's an X-ray of Carol's head. You can see the probes."

On the celluloid sheets before me were two images of Carol's skull, one taken from the front and one taken from the side. The frontal image clearly showed two, stark-white lines entering from the top of her head and con-verging to an area deep within her brain. The side image showed only one line, which indicated how precisely the two probes were aligned.

"Now all that's left is to tunnel the wires and insert the stimulators," she said. "They've put her under, but they tell me they were sad to do it, because she has been a real treat," she charmed. "Dr. McCarthy said Carol was crack-ing jokes the whole time!"

I could see that she allayed some of the uneasiness my son was feeling. I was, however, still focused on the X-rays before me. The images showed only one set of Carol's incisions sutured together with staples.

"Oh, I'm sure they took that X-ray before they had finished closing them," she answered when I inquired about the discrepancy.

Many hours later, my son and I finally got to see Carol in the recovery room. It was close to eight o'clock in the evening. She was groggy, as one would expect. The halo had been removed, and her head was bandaged with tier upon tier of gauze. It looked like a huge beehive. I kissed her and told her I'd see her in the morning.

The next day morning, I arrived in the ICU and met Dr. McCarthy while he was making his rounds.

"Dr. Keyloun!" he called to me. "Good morning. How are you?" He came over and shook my hand.

"I'm fine, fine. Thank you. A little tired. You?"

"A little tired, yes." He winked.

"So, how is everything?" I asked.

"It went very well. It took us a little longer than we expected to triangulate the probes, as you know, but there were no major complications."

"That's good to hear."

"I am going to have to transfuse her, though."

"Transfuse her? Why?"

"Well, she looks a little pale, and her blood count shows that her hematocrit is twenty-five."

Carol's preoperative hematocrit was forty-two, a normal level for her gender.

"Did she vomit blood?" I asked.

"No."

"Did she defecate blood?"

"No."

"Was there evidence of hemolysis?"

"No, no, nothing like that."

"So she must have lost blood in the operating room," I conjectured.

He bristled. "Excessive bleeding during neurosurgery never happens." He seemed to puff his chest at the offence of my suggestion and proclaimed, "Brain surgery is essentially a bloodless operation."

I looked at him for a few seconds before I directed, "I do not want her transfused." I had no confidence in the purity of the blood supply. While new tests for HIV were coming online and considered accurate, the risk of undetected hepatitis concerned me more. I knew that a good diet and supplemental iron in due time would restore her blood count.

He offered no rebuttal. He just walked away.

Later, an internist from the team came in to check up on Carol.

"Mrs. Keyloun, how are you feeling?" he inquired.

"I'm all right, thank you, Doctor."

"Well, you look terrific. I've got to tell you, even though the stimulators aren't on yet, you have so much more animation to your face already. It's just remarkable. I'm so excited for you, I really am!"

The doctor reminded us that Carol's neurostimulators would not be turned on for at least two weeks, until they were confident that any swelling in her brain had subsided, but he instructed us to return in eight days to have the sutures removed.

As he was leaving, I pulled him aside to ask about Carols's blood count. Since he had not been in the operating room, he said she could not comment if there was any blood loss, and offered no explanation for Carols' abrupt onset of anemia. It seemed of concern to no one that almost half of Carol's red cell volume had disappeared overnight. Nobody owned up to its whereabouts.

I took Carol home. Eight days later, we braved the elements of December and returned to NYU. Dr. McCarthy made small talk as he unwound the layers of gauze that covered Carol's head.

"You know, we had a contest in the O.R."

"Really?" I replied.

"Yes, it was the old fogies versus the young kids. My team used traditional sutures on her head, and the other team used metal clips." That explained the staples on only one side of the X-ray of Carol's skull. "They bet me they could close the wound faster!"

I had everything to do not to punch him in the face.

Dr. McCarthy removed the sutures in Carol's scalp and on her chest. With Christmas fast approaching, I asked him if there was any possibility that the neurostimulators could be turned on a few days sooner than the prescribed two weeks. Inspecting Carol's wounds, Dr. McCarthy replied, "These are healing very well, so I don't see any reason why you couldn't. I'll let Dr. Stancic know to schedule you for next week, OK?"

I arranged to bring Carol to New York by limousine. I was far too nervous to drive. The limo driver could not have been nicer, or more accommodating. He immediately took control. He took the wheelchair from me, wheeled Carol from the house to his car, and assisted her as she stumbled awkwardly into the front seat. At the hospital, he helped her out of the car again and into the wheelchair, and steered her as close to the curb as possible. Snow had fallen two days prior and had been shoveled into a mound at the curb. The driver held Carol's hand and almost carried her over the small embankment, as she clumsily navigated the snow to the cleared sidewalk where I had the wheelchair waiting. As I wheeled her into the hospital he shouted, "Good Luck!"

Carol sat in her wheelchair in Dr. Stancic's examination room. I stood behind her, and Dr. Stancic sat at a small desk. In his hands he held a small computer tablet that had a wand attached to it by a short electrical cord. With a stylus he punched data into the tablet, programming the voltage, interval and frequency of the electronic pulses to be delivered to Carol's brain. He then held the wand over the left side of Carol's chest in the vicinity of the neurostimulator. With a flourish, he tapped the tablet with the stylus. All at once, the tremor in her right hand disappeared! It was inconceivable. Dr. Stancic repeated the process on the right neurostimulator, and in an instant, Carol's left side stopped shaking. It was magical. Everyone smiled. Everyone was on the verge of tears.

What he said next sounded biblical.

"I want you to get up from your wheelchair and walk down the hall."

Carol looked at him, stunned. At first she was reluctant, but giddiness quickly overcame her. She slowly lifted herself from her wheelchair and strode down the length of the hall unattended. Dr. Stancic grabbed his video camera, and pressing the "Record" button, shouted, "Isn't this amazing!"

As often as I had been witness to surgical triumphs before, none compared with the exhilaration I was feeling at that moment. I watched my wife walk unescorted for the first time in years, and tears welled up and flowed freely down my cheeks.

Carol insisted on walking out of the hospital by herself. After years of walkers and wheelchairs, she ached for the sheer pleasure of it. Our limo driver stood waiting at the front entrance to the hospital. When he saw Carol walk through the door, he nearly passed out, and had to lean back against his limousine to support himself. The expression on his face was that of one who had just witnessed a miracle. I pushed the empty wheelchair down the handicap ramp and gave it to the driver, hoping I would never have to use it again. We drove home and began the slow road toward adjusting to a new life.

That Christmas was one of the best ever.

A Tale of Two Valves

One of the oddities of nature is the relationship between a Streptococcus infection and a diseased heart valve. Before the discovery of penicillin, a person with an upper respiratory infection due to a particular strain of the streptococcus bacteria would have to suffer the natural progression of the illness. After a couple of days with high fever, difficulty swallowing, and coughing, the body's immune system would eventually come to its defense and put out the fire. Unfortunately, the immune system sometimes never shut itself off. Years later (in most cases, decades later), the same patient might begin to experience difficulty breathing. Climbing stairs or running to catch the bus might result in shortness of breath. He or she might even have heard a wheeze when breathing, especially when stressed. These symptoms are the result of rheumatic heart disease, caused by the immune system's predilection to damage the mitral valve.

Alexander was a sixty-two-year old man who came to my office to get a refill for his asthma medication. He was under the care of a local doctor in Greenwich Village who had gone on vacation. The good doctor had failed to notify his patients that he would be away, and neglected to leave anyone in charge of his practice in his absence. Somehow, Alexander got my name as someone who would renew his prescription.

Alexander ran an auto rental agency on Fourteenth Street. He was an affable gentleman, slight of build, and quite deferential. He was married and had two grown children. When I asked him what his complaint was, he replied that he had suffered with asthma for many years, and that his doctor had prescribed something that "opened his lungs." He told me that, even though the medicine was not very effective, he had been told that it was all that could be done for his chronic condition, and that he would have to learn to live within the limits of his illness. I went through my usual list of questions, and learned he had no problems in any other organ system. The consultation completed, I asked Alexander to go to my examining room.

"Is an examination necessary?" he asked.

With a nod toward humor, I replied, "We don't charge extra for the exam."

He smiled.

Alexander was sitting on the examination table when I entered. He remained fully clothed. His feet were dangling over the side, and he swung them pendulum style from side to side. He was clearly anxious.

"Why don't you remove your shirt so I can examine you?"

"I have never removed my shirt," he boasted.

"How does your doctor examine you, then?"

"He just puts that 'listening thing' on my chest and listens."

"Through your shirt and undershirt?"

It wasn't how I was taught to perform an examination. I would have failed my final exam had I done anything like that. I started to doubt the quality of care he had been receiving.

"Well, Alex, in this office we get naked. Take off your shirts. Let's see some skin."

He stripped down to expose his chest.

He smiled.

His blood pressure was normal. His pulse was feeble. I placed my stethoscope on his chest and asked that he take deep breaths. As he exhaled, I could easily detect a faint wheeze. It could be heard diffusely in both lungs. To the casual observer, he had the telltale sign of asthma.

I listened to his heart while he was sitting up and while he was recumbent. More importantly, I listened while he was rolled over on his left side. In that position, I heard the murmur known as a "diastolic rumble." The sound is indicative of a narrowed mitral valve, the valve situated between the upper and lower chambers on the left side of the heart. I could also hear a third heart sound. Normally, when one listens to the heart, there is a classic "lub-dub" cadence. In Alexander's case, there was a "lub-duh-da" cadence. The third sound, called an "opening snap," is produced by a stiff mitral valve, and is never normal. Coupled with the diastolic rumble, there was little doubt that Alexander had rheumatic heart disease, and specifically, mitral stenosis, a pathologic narrowing of the mitral valve. The disease is progressive, and unless corrected, the patient will eventually suffer irreversible heart failure.

I reached two conclusions from my examination: one, it reinforced the aphorism "all that wheezes is not asthma," and two, Alexander had been misdiagnosed for years and would require open-heart surgery.

A few minutes later, Alexander was back in my consultation room, sitting across from my desk.

"You know, Doc, no one has ever examined me like you did."

He smiled.

"Well, Alex, that's the way I was taught. There are no short cuts. You either do it right or don't do it at all."

"So, what did you find out?"

I could not help but reflect on the irony. A nice guy comes to my office thinking all he needs is a prescription refill, but I'm about to tell him he needs open-heart surgery. What were the odds of that happening? How was I going to handle this one?

Tactfully.

I explained what was wrong with him, why he wheezed, why he was short of breath and why his medication was of no value. He took the news very well. In fact, he seemed relieved. He was glad that there was a repairable anatomical problem. I suppose his being in the auto industry helped. In his view, if an oil pump was malfunctioning, all one needed to do was to replace it. Knowing he had a malfunctioning mitral valve, it was completely logical to him that it be replaced.

Alexander underwent cardiac catheterization to confirm the diagnosis of advanced mitral stenosis. Several weeks later, once he had made arrangements for his business and put his personal affairs in order, he underwent surgery. The diseased valve was removed, and an artificial valve was inserted between the left atrium and ventricle. He made an uneventful recovery and was discharged from the hospital without complications.

Alexander returned to my office one month later to tell me he never felt so well. He couldn't remember a time when he had so much energy. He was breathing effortlessly. He was taking long walks with his wife. And—the happiest news of all—he was able to resume his sex life.

He smiled. Broadly.

Mitral valve surgery began as a crude operation where a surgeon inserted a finger into the left atrium through a purse string suture. He would blindly "fracture" the valve, thus opening it sufficiently to allow unrestricted blood flow. The difficulty was that the surgeon had no way of knowing how adequate was the opening he created: too small, and the entire procedure would be useless, too large and blood from the ventricle would regurgitate back into the atrium. Additionally, the crude procedure often dislodged cellular debris that served as an embolus to the brain, causing a stroke. Surgery of this sort often replaced one problem with another. But once a reliable artificial valve became available, the heartbeat could be arrested and the left atrium opened. This allowed the surgeon to visually inspect the valve, remove it, and suture a ball-in-cage valve in place of the diseased valve.

Sandra had already known of her cardiac condition for decades when she first came to me. Fortunately for her, the disease had progressed slowly. She was able to accommodate the limitations her heart imposed, and she fashioned her life around what her heart allowed her to do. However, she knew she would ultimately need surgery, and that with each passing decade, the risk-reward ratio skewed more heavily towards risk. I didn't have to point that out to her. Sandra was knowledgeable, astute, and well versed in the natural progression of her disease.

However, Sandra was reluctant. She had a responsible job at a major insurance company. She was nervous about open-heart surgery. She lived alone, with nobody in her life who she felt comfortable calling on to assist her during her convalescence. She had a sister who lived far away in Saskatchewan, Canada, but she was either unable or unwilling to help. But, while the reasons for Sandra's reticence were of some concern, they certainly were not insurmountable.

In an attempt to alleviate her fear, I spent several months introducing Sandra to the cardiac surgeon, the surgical team, the group in social service, and members of the visiting nurse service. I arranged a walk-through of the operating suite and the post-operative recovery area of the coronary care unit. In short, she was taken on a complete tour of where she would be at every step of her time in the hospital. I thought the familiarity with the people and the surroundings would serve to reassure Sandra, but she confessed that she was still hesitant to go ahead with the procedure.

She did, however, undergo cardiac catheterization, and the resultant data indicated that postponement was not a prudent option. Her case was presented at the weekly "cath conference," where all the cases of the preceding week were reviewed by a broad group of cardiologists and cardiac surgeons. It was a unanimous vote that Sandra needed surgery, and she needed it as soon as possible. The committee's collective decision finally convinced her to accelerate the timing of her surgery.

Sandra was taken by gurney to the operating room at seven o'clock in the morning. She was transferred to the operating table sometime around seven-thirty, and surgery began. The procedure was uneventful. She was disconnected from the heart-lung machine and wheeled to the CCU around eleven o'clock in the morning.

The nurses in intensive care immediately confronted problems. Her blood pressure was barely audible. She was unable to trigger the respirator. (Normally, a patient coming out of anesthesia is assisted by a respirator that is activated by the patient's natural initiation of breath. Unable to inspire, Sandra's respirator had to be programmed to breathe for her.) Most worrisome of all, she was not waking up.

The cardiac surgeon was called to come to the bedside, but he had already begun another operation. It was hours later when he appeared. He had no idea why Sandra was laboring as she was. He ordered an X-ray of her chest. Because she was in the CCU, hooked up to a respirator, monitors and tubes, she could not be transported to the radiology department, so a portable machine had to be brought to her bedside. Radiology was on the second floor of an adjacent building. It was nearly one o'clock in the afternoon before the machine finally arrived in the CCU on the tenth floor. Once the X-ray was taken, the machine and the plate were wheeled back to the radiology department, where the plate was developed. At last, the film was returned to the CCU for interpretation.

The cardiac surgeon had sewn in the artificial mitral valve *upside down!*

Valves in the heart are designed to restrict blood flow to one-way, forward movement. An artificial valve that is inserted upside down instead works like a dam, stopping forward blood flow altogether. Sandra was rushed back to the operating room, where she underwent a second open-heart operation to correct the catastrophic error.

I was notified of the disaster soon after the second operation had begun. When she returned to the CCU, it was nearly eight o'clock in the evening. She had been in surgery, under anesthesia, for the better part of nine hours. She had received countless blood transfusions, and had virtually no forward blood flow from the time she left the operating suite at eleven o'clock that morning until she was reattached to the heart-lung machine nearly four hours later.

Sandra never regained consciousness.

There are no words to exonerate the most egregious surgical malfeasance of my entire medical career. There are no words to properly express remorse. There are no words to voice my outrage.

Sandra's death took an emotional toll on me, and Rose did everything in her power to buffer my anger. She shared it. After office hours, we sat together at the bar in Carmine's on Greenwich Avenue, across the street from the hospital. The martinis did nothing to diminish our outrage. The booze only reinforced it.

"What do you think will happen?" I asked.

"Nothing!"

"Nothing? He should at least lose his admitting privileges."

"Victor, Victor, Victor, look at me!" I lifted my eyes from the bottom of my glass to face her. "It's never gonna happen. You know goddamn well what the politics are."

She knew the cardiac surgeon would never be reprimanded. He was too valuable to the hospital, the only one on staff qualified to perform open-heart surgery.

Her perception was right on target. I naively thought that such an inconceivable act of surgical malfeasance would generate an appropriate punishment, but the cardiac surgeon continued to do surgery. He was neither reprimanded nor suspended

I notified her sister of Sandra's passing. She could have easily sued for malpractice, if not wrongful death, and won uncontested, but she had no interest in the pursuit of it. She elected not to come to New York to claim the body. Sandra was buried according to the directions in her last will and testament.

Her case continues to haunt me.

The Lady in Blue

A diaphanous, cobalt blue silk blouse hung from her shoulders. Her hands were adorned with rings on each long, pencil-thin finger. Jet black curls hung in soft ringlets, framing her face. Perfectly arched eyebrows crowned two sparkling brown eyes, each lined in black pencil and shadowed with a blue blush on the upper lids. Her lips were glossed fuchsia, and the diamond pendant earrings she wore glittered in the afternoon sun. My eyes were riveted by this lovely woman I found sitting on the sofa in my waiting room.

I breezed past her towards my office, stopping for a moment to catch my secretary's eyes. With only body gestures and a paucity of words, I asked Rose if she knew who the lady in blue was. She whispered, "New," and with a cocked eyebrow added, "Seems nice."

I sat at my desk to ready myself for the afternoon's assault. I had spent the morning making rounds at the hospital. Now I had to attend the twenty patients scheduled for the day, and address God only knows how many emergencies that would crop up. This was going to be a seven o'clock day, maybe eight o'clock. I ordered in lunch and turned to the piles of mail on my desk. That which required only a signature was quickly dispatched. Junk mail received only a brief perusal before it was tossed into the circular file beneath the desk. Anything that remained was placed in my briefcase for the train ride home. This mail tended to find its way to my porch to be dealt with on Sunday afternoon.

Rose came in with a stack of papers, and began to entertain me with endless chatter about her family intrigue, boyfriends, love life, and the most recent neighborhood gossip, all the while collating through her stack, identifying the line to which I should affix my signature. The paperwork completed, I signaled to her that it was about time we began to see the patients who were rapidly filling the waiting room. I had instructed her countless times to space appointments every twenty minutes, but it always seemed that ten people were outside clamoring to be seen first.

The woman in blue entered my consultation room. Now I noticed that she wore black silk pants and black velvet pumps. It occurred to me that she was overly dressed to see a doctor. I was fortunate to have a good practice with predominantly middle-class patients. This patient was dressed well enough in the middle of the day to attend an evening formal at the Waldorf Astoria.

She introduced herself as Georgina Ross. She had no present complaint to speak of, and it seemed that she had suffered no serious illness in the past. She merely wanted to establish a relationship with a doctor in case she ever really needed one, and a friend of hers had recommended me. She was smart, thoughtful, and articulate. Throughout the consultation, I was struck by Georgina's femininity. Her gestures, her speech, and her mannerisms were all precise. As I led her to the examining room across the corridor, I noticed a peculiar sway in her pelvis as she walked.

Starting from her head and working my way down, the examination was routinely normal until I reached her breasts. There was a resiliency to them that was unmistakable. They were silicone implants. This was not the first time a woman neglected to tell me that she had undergone breast augmentation. When the procedure was first introduced, it was almost a clandestine affair. Women only spoke about it in the most private conversations, and very few plastic surgeons performed it. Many of my patients would wait until I discovered them, and then sheepishly confess that they had implants. Later, when it became a routine phenomenon, almost a craze in New York during the early 1970s, attitudes changed. It became a test. Often women would ask, "Hey Doc, what do you think of my boob job?" It was an impossible question. If I said, "They're beautiful," I'd be a lecher. And if I said, "Why did you bother?" the insult was liable to send her bolting from the examining table and out the door. Most times I chose to ignore the question.

When I asked Georgina about her implants, she casually responded that she had some work done by a plastic surgeon. I continued with my examination, all the while maintaining a superficial dialogue. As I wended my way down to her pelvis, I noticed her hips had the same consistency as her breasts, and the symmetry of her escutcheon was askew. I was beginning to think that I was the brunt of a bad joke.

"Georgina," I asked, "just how much plastic surgery have you had?"

"You noticed," she said.

"I have more than a casual knowledge of human anatomy," I said, "even if I weren't a doctor."

She laughed as if she had just heard the punch line of a long-winded joke.

"I am transsexual," she said. I stood there, dumbfounded.

"Why didn't you say something about it when we talked in my consultation room?"

"I wanted to see how perceptive you were," she said. "I measure a doctor by how fast he gets to the truth."

I wondered how I would be measured, considering it took a physical examination of her naked body for me to realize what was plainly true. I had dismissed all of the signs I had seen. Georgina had an Adam's apple. The rings on her fingers offset wide knuckles. Her mannerisms and speech patterns were almost too feminine. But I chose to ignore it all, instead accepting at face value the illusion that Georgina created. Perhaps that was the point.

Once I completed my examination on Georgina, we reconvened in my consultation room, where I asked for a more in-depth history. Georgina had been born George Majewski, and lived as a man for the first twenty-four years of her life. During George's teenage years, he thought he was gay, because he never found himself attracted to women. He moved to New York City, and gravitated to Greenwich Village, like so many gay men before him. He was certain that he could find fulfillment and acceptance within the subculture there. He had several homosexual liaisons, but none was satisfying. Sexually deprived and emotionally unfulfilled, he became profoundly depressed. George sought psychiatric counseling. In working through the depths of his depression, George realized that his were not the emotions of a gay man, but rather those of a heterosexual woman. After several years in therapy, he was convinced more than ever that he was meant to go through life as a woman. It wasn't about anatomy; it was a matter of identity.

When his courage was at its zenith, he confronted his parents. Breaking this kind of news to a macho Polish father and a Hispanic mother with absolutely no understanding or compassion was no easy task. He didn't so much seek their approval as formally announce his intentions. They were not happy. In fact, they disowned him.

He began his transformation by wearing women's clothes to work. He walked in one Monday morning and announced that he was no longer to be called George. He was now Georgina. After the snickering abated, his fellow employees asked what the joke was all about and how large the bet he lost had been. But after several weeks of seeing Georgina in women's clothes, colleagues in the workplace were convinced that it was the real thing. While Georgina assumed the external, superficial trappings of a female, she also began to take diethyl stilbesterol, an early form of artificial estrogen. Within months, the coarse curly hair on her arms and legs faded into fine wisps, her musculature softened, her voice raised, and her male libido disappeared.

There was always the consideration that George may have made a mistake. Each step in the transition was planned such that a change of heart would not be met with an irrevocable anatomic alteration. In her first surgery, silicone breasts were implanted. The emotional exhilaration that ensued was fuel to the fire roaring within her. Finally, her body was starting to reflect how she felt. She could wear a brassiere. Dresses and blouses fit so much better. She was starting to look less like a "boy in a dress" and more like a real woman. Her wardrobe grew in proportion to the compliments she received and the wolf-whistles she got in public. The flattery was intoxicating.

After a year of presenting herself as a woman, it was time for the ultimate decision. Until now all that was done could be undone. Now it was the time, if there ever was a time, for George to become Georgina anatomically. The psychiatrist, psychologist and social worker each declared that she was of stable mind and was making a rational decision. Relatives and friends lent moral support, which helped immeasurably to counter the rejection by her parents. All lent guidance to help her make the proper decision. The correct decision. But it was already made in her heart. George had to be Georgina.

In the first of five operations, George had his penis amputated and his testicles removed. A flap was created from skin on his abdomen and fashioned into a tube. Once the blood supply had matured, a second surgery rotated the tube and advanced it to the perineum. In the third operation, the flap was fashioned into a functional vagina and inserted into Georgina's pelvis. After this surgery, he had his name changed legally to Georgina, and his gender officially changed to female. There were several more operations to tidy up the vaginal implant so that it could receive a penis. And finally, silicone was injected at the *mons pubis* and around the hips to give her the added appearance of a female pelvis. (Gender reassignment surgery has fortunately come a long way in these intervening years. It is an infinitely more refined procedure today.)

Georgina got married to a man who loved her very much. He was remarkably handsome. To say her husband was handsome is to betray some of my own prejudice, because my first inclination was to wonder who would marry a transsexual except some guy who couldn't find anything better. Prejudice such as mine might lead me to believe he had to be a loser. Nothing was further from the truth. Ben Ross was well-to-do. He owned a zipper factory that supplied the garment industry. He was shorter than his Georgina by several inches, but he was muscular and well-proportioned. Curly salt and pepper hair topped a cherubic, round face. His blue eyes were deep set, and his nose was large but straight. When he smiled, he revealed a set of small, sparkling, perfectly symmetrical white teeth. His clothes were tailored and very fashionable. I suspected they were also very expensive. His simple conservative style stood in stark contrast to Georgina's pearl necklaces, redundant bracelets, rings, and brooches that she wore at all times (or at least every time she came to see me).

I first met Ben when he accompanied Georgina to a checkup. As the three of us sat together in my consultation room, my curiosity got the better of me. I couldn't help wondering if sex with a man with a make-believe vagina was anything like having sex with a woman born with the requisite anatomy.

"Do you have sexual intercourse?" I asked, stupidly.

They looked at each other and laughed. I felt a pressing need to retreat.

"What I mean to say is, do you have any difficulties having sexual intercourse?"

"No," Ben answered with a smile. "Everything works as it should. Besides, in the heat of the moment, Doctor, you don't concentrate on what is different, but on what joins you together."

I was grateful for his affability.

Georgina and Ben were above average intellects. Each had a grasp of reality that far eclipsed mine. After all, until Georgina walked into my office, I had only read about transgender in the medical literature. Like so many others, I had followed the exploits of Christine Jorgensen in the newspapers, the first person to publicly acknowledge that she had undergone sexual reassignment. In 1952 her story was splashed across the tabloids and became the subject of endless discussions and debates. She was a novelty, and I saw her as such. But sitting across from me, the Rosses were real people, living their life fully. I resolved never in a moment of idle curiosity to ask another senseless question like that again.

For all the time she was my patient, Georgina was never ill other than the occasional cold or sinus headache. She came to see me like any other housewife, sometimes just to talk about the drudgery of her routine or to get a little reassurance. From time to time, she came to vent her concerns about being a good wife. We talked about her feelings as much as time would allow. She taught me so much about the difference between the male view and the female view of life. After all, she had a very unique perspective. She reassured me that a lot of it is hormonal. But she recalled vividly how she had felt on the other side of the gender divide.

One afternoon, I saw Georgina for a peculiar headache at the bridge of her nose. She described it as similar to a sinus headache, but without the usual congestion or runny nose. The examination yielded no salient information, so I prescribed an antihistamine and reassured her that if it was not better, we might send her to an ear, nose, and throat specialist.

A few weeks later, I returned home from a long, well-deserved weekend vacation with my family. The suitcases were unpacked and the mail was opened. I had just sat down with the *Times*, to relish the quiet of the evening after a long drive, when the phone rang. Dr. Larson, who covered my practice during my absence, called to sign off for the weekend. He ran down the list of patients in the hospital, gave me a progress report on each, and finished by saying that Georgina Ross was in the emergency room, but he did not see her since he knew I would be home shortly. I paid it no mind, assuming that she had presented in the E.R. for some trivial weekend problem, having not been able to reach me. Maybe she lacerated a finger or twisted an ankle, I thought. If it was important, the resident physician would have called me. He hadn't, so I decided to go to bed. The bed was warm and so was my wife. Our son was asleep and my mind drifted to other pleasures.

The phone rang in the midst of our lovemaking.

"What?" I snapped into the receiver.

"Dr. Keyloun, it's Dr. Robinson in the E.R.," came the apologetic voice. "I'm sorry to disturb you, but your patient Georgina Ross is here."

"Well, I hope it's important enough to call me in the middle of the night!"

"Well, sir, she's in a coma."

"What?" Composing myself I asked, "What are you talking about?"

Dr. Robinson told me that Georgina's husband had come home that afternoon and thought she was asleep, so he left her alone for about an hour. When it was way past dinner time, he tried to rouse her, but couldn't, so he called the police and they dispatched an ambulance.

By now, I was sitting at the side of my bed.

"What have you found so far?" I asked calmly, almost plaintively, feeling a bit guilty for having chastised the poor resident.

"Not much. She is totally unresponsive. No lateralizing signs. Vital signs are normal. This doesn't look like an overdose. We are going to send her for a C-T scan and I'll get back to you with the results."

"Thank you," I said. I hung up the phone and lay back in bed. There was no sense trying to recapture the moments lost. Carol rubbed my shoulder and we both fell off to sleep.

No other call came that night. The alarm rang as usual, and I thought, *Maybe it was the wrong patient. Maybe someone made a mistake. Maybe she woke up and went home. That's why no one called me with a report.*

The commute into Manhattan on the Long Island Railroad seemed interminable that morning. The newspaper held no interest for me, and I couldn't wait to get off the goddamned train and get to work. At last, we screeched into Pennsylvania Station, where I became one of the herd, lowing on its way to the downtown express. Fortunately, it was only one stop. My breakfast of coffee and an English muffin sat like clay in the pit of my stomach. We lurched into the Fourteenth Street station, and a mass of humanity rocked counter to the momentum of the train, causing us a momentary and unwelcome physical familiarity with one another. The train doors opened and I bounded up the steps of the station and made a beeline for the viewing room in C-T Scanning.

The films were in the jacket, filed appropriately in the proper alphabetical slot. *At least they weren't lost somewhere in X-ray, like they usually are*, I thought, annoyed that I hadn't received a call with the results as I had been promised. I placed the sheets of film on the viewing box and there before my eyes was a celluloid nightmare.

"A subarachnoid hemorrhage," a nameless neurological resident who, by chance, was in the viewing room whispered to me over my shoulder, "from a ruptured AVM."

Georgina Ross' entire left cerebral hemisphere was destroyed. Half of her brain was mush. She had suffered a hemorrhage into her brain from an arterio-venous malformation. I stood transfixed. The coffee and English muffin threatened a second appearance. I screwed up all the courage I could muster and walked up the stairs to the fourth floor to face Ben Ross and the family.

The scene in the hospital room was a tableau. Georgina was in bed, a picture of serenity. Her hair was neatly combed. The blankets and sheets were smooth and tucked. Her right arm was on top of her blanket; her fingernails polished a brilliant red. Ben held her left hand. He was sitting at the bedside, staring at the wall. It could have been a scene in their apartment's bedroom. The only evidence that destroyed the illusion was the endotracheal tube connected to a softly soughing respirator. It was the only thing keeping her alive.

I walked up behind Ben and squeezed his shoulders. He stood up mechanically, turned to face me, and began to cry. Only the cement in my stomach kept me from joining him. When Ben's tears had been spent, we walked out into the corridor, where I was not greeted with the usual barrage of nonsensical questions. I was asked instead only two things: What makes an AVM bleed, and was there any way we might have known this could happen?

There is a time and place for dissertations and lengthy pronouncements, but the absolute wrong time and wrong place is outside the room of a dying patient with a grieving spouse. It was not the time to tell him that one in one hundred thousand people has an AVM, a congenital malformation in which the small arteries and veins in the brain are abnormally connected to each other. Of those, only the AVMs that bleed receive the attention of the medical profession. We have no idea how many sudden deaths are due to AVM rupture, nor do we know how many people live a normal life and die of some other malady. It was not the time to tell him there was nothing unique about her presenting headache that would have lead anyone towards an exhaustive investigation. Even if the AVM were detected, was it amenable to surgery? And what about the risks of surgery itself? It was not the time to tell Ben that I had a college classmate who fell overboard while sailing, and was presumed to have drowned, until the autopsy showed he ruptured an AVM. Nor was it the time to tell him that a current member of the house staff had ruptured an aneurysm, bled, and survived the ordeal with all his intellect intact. It was time only to comfort him and share the vigil.

"I don't know, Ben," I said, shaking my head. "Maybe we should see what fate has in store, and later I can provide some definitive answers."

Georgina Ross died five days after she was admitted to the hospital.

There were no recriminations from the family, only questions. They were all variations of "Could you have known?" Wasn't her headache a tip-off that something was wrong? Should she have had an angiogram? Would surgery have saved her?

But how can a doctor exhaustively investigate everyone with a headache? There was nothing unique about her complaint. How many angiograms would have to be performed? Even if something were detected, would it be amenable to surgery? Would the patient be left with permanent neurological deficits? And what about the risks of surgery itself?

The longer one is in private practice, the less secure are the answers to the flood of endless questions. One hundred years ago, the responsibility of a physician was to comfort his patient as much as to treat him. Patients expected little from their physicians. Cures were few, and surgery was as much mutilating as it was beneficial. Today, the razzle-dazzle of the marketplace has thrust physicians into an unrealistic role of omnipotence. Ben Casey and Dr. Kildare never lost a patient on their TV series. They cured every exotic disease that they encountered. Medical advance, proven worthwhile or not, is prime-time news on every television channel.

Dealing with the reality of death becomes a game played against a stacked deck, because all the scientific advances of the past fifty years seem to have bestowed upon the medical profession the idea of infallibility. Weren't patients being resuscitated from death with cardiac massage? Weren't hearts being transplanted? Wasn't each new antibiotic a more spectacular wonder drug capable of destroying any germ?

"Doctor, why did my father die of pneumonia?"

"Well, Miss James, your dad had emphysema from smoking three packs of cigarettes a day for forty years. The pneumonia was incidental to his death."

In Miss James' eyes was the finality of a pounding gavel. You can surmise her judgment. *That's not an acceptable answer. You could have cured him.*

"Doctor, why did my wife die of hepatitis? She was only twenty-eight years old."

"Well, Mr. Smith, we have no cure for hepatitis, and there is no effective treatment."

Again, the gavel strikes. *Don't tell me my expectation is more than you can deliver.*

Our expectations are raised by technology: respirators that will keep alive the smokers who abused themselves for half a century; kidney machines that will keep alive elderly patients who have no sense of who or where they are; mechanical hearts that promise life, but in reality only last but a few weeks and reduce their human recipients to the equivalent of a laboratory animal.

The gavel pounds for them too, but now the judgment is in reverse. *Doctor, you must stop this living hell! You never told me that living like this would be so painful!*

The gavel pounds in the eyes of every patient. A judgment is made with every doctor-patient interaction. Whether treated for a cold or for cancer, the patient judges and the family judges. The transcendent question is whether the judgment is fair.

The Triangle Twists

Ten years is a long time to care for a family. With such longevity, the doctor-patient bond evolves into a bona fide relationship, of sorts. Language becomes more subtle, behavior more nuanced. Visits become more casual, more routine, even mundane. But the longer patients returned to me for care, the more woven into each others' lives we became.

It had been ten years since Tina Bellini first came to me for her shot of B_{12}. In that time, I took her through a repair of a femoral hernia and gallbladder surgery, both uneventfully. Her husband, Pasquale, underwent cataract surgery. His left leg went cold several years after his unsuccessful surgery. He could barely walk a half a block and then only slowly and in pain. He ceased working and collected disability income. He took a few non-strenuous jobs off the books to supplement his income. He stopped neither smoking nor drinking.

Her daughters, Philomena and Edwina, never suffered anything more serious than the flu. About four years into our relationship, Philomena came to my office and casually requested birth control pills. She never refilled the prescription through me, so I never knew whether it was a one-time romance or something long-term. She never married. Edwina continued to be a secretary. She learned that the gonorrhea her physician lover passed to her had been contracted from someone other than his wife. It took her a full two years to accept the fact that he was cheating on her, too, and to toss him to the curb.

I finally met the third daughter, Catherina. While visiting her parents on Staten Island one weekend, her husband was seized by excruciating abdominal pain. Knowing no other physician in New York, they elected to come to the St. Vincent's emergency room. It required a bus ride to the ferry terminal, the ferry ride across New York Harbor and a subway ride from Battery Park—a weekend journey of at least one and a half hours. They called me to see him. He lay motionless with pain. His skin was cold and clammy. His abdomen was as rigid as a board. The level of amylase in his blood and urine was markedly elevated. He was suffering with acute pancreatitis. Catherina had married an alcoholic just like her daddy. Her husband survived his ordeal and was advised to quit drinking. I had very little conversation with Catherina except at her husband's bedside, but I did tell her that the next episode of pancreatitis could be fatal. They returned to the Caribbean and I did not hear from her again until years later.

During all those years and all those visits and endless hours of conversation, the triangle of abuse persisted. Pasquale continued the abuse, the daughters endured it, and Tina excused it. I could get none of them to understand it. The daughters were intelligent, yet something prevented them from gaining any insight.

The long years of neglecting his doctor's advice, drinking and smoking ultimately led to a crisis. Pasquale appeared in the emergency room, ashen and diaphoretic. He was perspiring as if he were in a sauna. He had been vomiting all night. He denied drinking, but Tina whispered in my ear that he had been on a binge for two continuous weeks.

Pasquale was a mess. He was dehydrated and, worst of all, the rhythm of his heart had changed. He had developed atrial fibrillation, a condition that renders the heartbeat totally irregular. It subjects the patient to the potential of blood clots forming in the heart and travelling to distant parts of the body. While many people live long lives with atrial fibrillation, Pasquale could ill afford an irregular rhythm coupled with his terrible circulatory problems. It was my conviction that this rhythm disturbance could spell the difference as to whether he kept or lost his legs.

I prescribed quinidine to regulate his heart. Quinidine is a chemical cousin of quinine, an alkaloid derived from the bark of the cinchona tree, and had been prescribed as an effective antiarrythmic for over fifty years. Side effects are well known, but the most devastating is the rapid destruction of platelets, the cells that help blood to clot. A person with depleted platelets can bleed to death from a laceration, or worse, bleed internally into vital organs. Fortunately the risk is rare, and I prescribed the drug with the reassurance that Pasquale would be under constant observation in the hospital. For five days, while I performed a number of studies on Pasquale's condition, this idyllic observation persisted. But on the morning of the sixth day, my patient announced he was going home.

"You are not ready," I said.

"I don't want no more of this hospital."

"This isn't a jail," I said, "I can't keep you against your will, but you're making a grave mistake."

I lost the argument. I called Tina at work and related the problem. She called Pasquale. She, too, lost the argument. Pasquale went home.

Two weeks later, I received a page on my beeper just as I entered the hospital. I answered it to hear Tina relate how Pasquale's skin had countless red blemishes on his hands and feet. My heart sank. As forcefully as I could, I directed Tina to bring Pasquale to my office. I interrupted hospital rounds to meet them, and to my dismay, observed a diffuse petecchial rash extending from his fingers up to mid-arm and from his toes to mid-thigh.

I quickly completed my examination and explained what was wrong. Pasquale was the one in one hundred thousand who reacted poorly to the quinidine. His symptoms hadn't yet progressed to alarming levels, but my most serious concern was that he could develop internal bleeding. I advised them that he had to be in the hospital for observation and treatment until his platelet count stabilized. I told them he might require blood transfusions, but that I couldn't be sure until certain blood tests were performed. I spoke in as pointed and direct manner as I could muster.

To my utter consternation (although I should not have been so surprised, given his prior behavior), Pasquale refused hospitalization. This time, however, was different. This time was truly a life-or-death situation. But no amount of explanation, cajoling, badgering, or instruction would convince Pasquale that the rash on his arms and legs threatened his very life.

"For God's sake Tina, have you no influence on him? Explain the seriousness of it to him in Italian," I begged her.

They mumbled a few phrases to each other, and she turned to me with a shrug and said, "He's a *testa dura*."

"I know that means a 'hard head' but frankly, it's more like an anvil."

They left the office to take the ferry back to Staten Island. As they were walking out, I wondered why he questioned my judgment. And why it bothered me so when it was ignored. Was it a flaw in my personality? Was my ego that fragile? Maybe I needed a few sessions on the couch with Charlie Ratigan.

The next morning my beeper went off. It did not take much intuition to know that it would be the Bellinis who called. Pasquale's nose was bleeding and it wouldn't stop. "God damn it!" I whispered. My worst nightmare had come true. I told Tina to get him to a hospital—any hospital—and have the emergency room physician call me. Philomena was at home and said she would drive him to St. Vincent's. "Hurry," I urged her.

More than an hour elapsed when my beeper chirped again. Tina was in a hospital in Brooklyn. Pasquale's bleeding was so severe that she didn't think he would make it to Manhattan. I told her it was just as well. The sooner he gets medical attention, the better.

"Remind the emergency room doctor about the quinidine," I instructed her, "and have him call me if he needs more information."

Everyone who has been in military service knows the meaning of the acronym "FUBAR." I learned it in the Navy. Fucked Up Beyond All Recognition. It's what happened to Pasquale's subsequent medical care at the other hospital. All they could see was an elderly man bleeding profusely from his nose. They asked him no questions and Tina offered no information. He was admitted to the ear, nose and throat service and had his nose packed, a useless misadventure. It was a full ten hours before anyone realized that Pasquale's platelet count was nonexistent, and it was yet another four hours before the hematologist began transfusing platelets and administering intravenous cortisone. But by then, Pasquale was bleeding everywhere, including into his brain. He died the next day.

Tina called me to say "Pasquale is no more." I expressed my condolence, commiserated with her, tried to comfort her, but I knew she wasn't listening. My mind wandered off to thoughts about blind stubbornness. On the one hand, dogged pursuit can be the wellspring of success, while on the other, it is often one's own undoing.

My philosophic musing came to an abrupt end when I heard Tina say, "What am I going to do now without Pasquale?" A most curious comment, I thought. I would have thought that after a lifetime of physical and mental abuse, after a lifetime of seeing her daughters' lives destroyed, she might for a brief moment feel a sense of relief. She might see a ray of hope for the future. What I heard instead was the first rumble that the triangle was shifting. I was to learn the true meaning of a parasitic relationship, that once it is disrupted, the surviving members look for someone to fill the void. I was to become the victim.

The phone rang at two in the morning. It was Catherina's voice on the phone and she was very drunk. She unleashed a tirade of abuse and invective that lasted for twenty minutes, wherein she accused me of killing her father. I said not one word. There was no hope of a meaningful conversation. There was no way to make her understand that her father's intransigence and her mother's failure to communicate basic information led to his demise. There was no way in the middle of the night to remind her that her father was a reluctant patient at best and an insanely stubborn one at worst. She needed to vent her anger, displaced as it may have been. When she exhausted herself, she hung up the phone.

By now Carol was wide awake. "What was that all about?" she asked. I told her not to be alarmed, but she persisted. It was a common occurrence for me to get calls in the middle of the night, dispense advice, and go right back to sleep. This time, I lingered on the phone and said nothing. I related the entire story. "This won't end well," she mumbled as we burrowed back under the covers. Her intuition was flawless.

The process server came to my office to deliver the subpoena. I was sued for malpractice. Rosina Bellini and Edwina, Philomena, and Catherina Bellini sued me on behalf of the Estate of Pasquale Bellini for "wrongful death."

I felt the blood drain from my face and my hands go numb. *How could this happen?* I began to panic. *What should I do? How should I respond?* I caught a glimpse of my reflection in the window. *I'm forty years old, for God's sake,* I thought. *I have to shave my beard. If I don't, they'll think I'm some kind of idiot, some Greenwich Village hippie who has no business practicing medicine!*

I ran to the bathroom and looked in the mirror. *No, my beard is gray! It makes me look professional, like a wise sage. I should keep it.*

I went back and forth like this in my office for the rest of the day. Such silly thoughts interfere with rational decisions in times of stress like these. I was confused, hurt, threatened, and insecure. My convictions wavered.

Looking about the office waiting room, I thought, *Who else here is the enemy?*

Then I realized if I could be sued for malpractice without legitimate reason after years of caring, what would happen if I ever did make a mistake? No matter how diligently I practiced medicine, the law of averages dictates that I will err. After all, I am human.

More and more thoughts clicked in my brain, muddling my mind even further.

On my way home that night, I finally reached some clarity, and a minor sense of calm. This case would not be resolved tonight, and it would never get to trial. No defense attorney would allow it. I somehow knew intuitively that a trial would have all the trappings of a B-grade movie: A wealthy, callous physician rendering cursory and superficial treatment victimizes poor and harried widow.

God damn it! I was being dehumanized for practicing good medicine, for having been compassionate, for having carried a family on my back for ten years, always making financial concessions, and never once being unavailable. Never once was their care given short shrift. Never once was any member hustled through my office or treated any differently from any other patient. The injustice was killing me.

The wind, I thought. *Go tell it to the wind because no one else gives a shit.*

About two years later the wheels of justice ground inexorably to the inevitable. Both Tina and I were deposed prior to trial. My attorney gave me the transcript of her deposition to read. According to her testimony, Pasquale was a paragon of virtue. He was the most supportive, loving, caring provider God ever put on the face of the earth. He worked like a dog to put bread on the table and never drank except at Christmas and Easter. And now, because of me, and what I did to him, she was deprived of his love and affection. And her daughters! How would they survive without his counsel and wisdom? How could they mature and fulfill their dreams without the benefit of their father's advice? This most orchestrated and well-rehearsed fairy tale went on for pages. Just by reading the text, I could see she had given a performance worthy of an Academy Award. I looked up at my attorney and just glared. We both knew it was all about the money. Pasquale's death became a lottery ticket. I could never have competed with this act at trial. My attorney settled the case.

I learned something new about human nature.

Malpractice

What is obvious to most fair-minded people engaged in the malpractice debate is that doctors make mistakes. We're human. Patients enter into a relationship expecting to receive competent care from their doctor or hospital, and sometimes the process goes awry. Sometimes, patients are egregiously injured. No reasonable person would suggest that such a victim not be compensated. Where the debate becomes contentious is defining what, exactly, constitutes medical malpractice, and how much should be the settlement.

There was a time when it seemed like every automobile accident resulted in a "whiplash" injury to the neck. Unscrupulous lawyers manufactured claims and pursued them assiduously under tort litigation. The awards were outrageous, and insurance premiums quickly and sharply escalated. Widespread public outrage ensued, and the legislature ultimately adopted and passed a no-fault statute. Anyone injured in an auto accident no longer had to prove negligence; their insurance carrier simply compensated them for damages. However, they could no longer sue for punitive damages, unless it could be proved that the injuries exceeded a certain defined threshold. Overnight, whiplash was removed from tort litigation, and a vast reservoir of claims evaporated. The last remaining pool of potential tort litigation was the medical profession.

No-fault standards for medical malpractice do not exist. Any attempts to adopt them have been met with dismal failure. Instead, we leave it to the judiciary system, whereby a jury of our "peers" determines whether malpractice has occurred, and what the value of such medical malfeasance should be. But what perspective or insight does a jury of non-medical professionals have to do so? How can a jury place a value on, say, operating on the wrong side of the brain, amputating the wrong leg, or leaving an instrument in the patient's abdomen?

The foregoing examples all fall under the category of *res ipsa loquitor*, meaning "it speaks for itself." There are no factual elements to prove; they are obvious cases of malpractice, and the legal case centers largely on how much can be negotiated in a settlement. However, many cases are less obvious, and these are largely to blame for the morass that medical malpractice torts have become.

A woman was referred to me because she had kidney disease. Her laboratory work indicated that she had compromised renal function, but it was not yet severe enough to warrant permanent dialysis. She had already received antibiotic treatment in another city, and had suffered some hearing loss as a result. In a quiet environment, she could carry on a conversation without difficulty, but she had trouble discerning words when ambient noise was present. She saw me every three months, and her condition remained stable.

During the second year of our relationship, she presented with severe abdominal pain and a high fever. Her blood work indicated that she had peritonitis that had spread to her blood stream. As a result of the systemic infection, her kidney function deteriorated markedly. I admitted her to the hospital for treatment. The only antibiotic effective against her particular infection was Kanamycin. It was a powerful drug, but it had a predilection to cause hearing loss. Its prescription was further complicated because it is excreted by the kidneys, and my patient had stopped making urine.

We instituted peritoneal dialysis. However, there was no algorithm that instructed how to administer Kanamycin in the face of renal failure. Given the degree of her kidney failure, I knew that her body would be unable to excrete a normal, intravenous dose of the drug, and she would surely suffer massive hearing loss. I consulted with colleagues, and together we came up with a decreasing logarithmic progression for administering the drug: the first dose was half the recommended starting dose, the second dose was half again as much, and the third dose was half as much again.

The plan worked. My patient recovered, and her blood work indicated that her kidney function returned to her pre-hospitalization status. She was soon discharged with all of her faculties seemingly intact. She had dodged a life-threatening bullet, and it was a marvel that she suffered no further damage to her kidneys. We felt a little proud of ourselves that we had managed to successfully navigate a difficult set of circumstances.

About three months later, I was summoned to the office of the Chief of Anesthesiology. I could not imagine why he called for me, but I interrupted my rounds and went straight to the operating suites where he conducted his business. In his office was a partner of the law firm that defended malpractice suits for members of the medical society. Apparently, they were friends. The inquisition began immediately.

"Dr. Keyloun, why do you make yourself so unavailable?" the Chief asked me.

"I'm sorry?"

"The father of your patient claims that he has tried on many occasions to contact you, and has been unable to reach you."

"You got me in person within ten minutes," I said, in a way that clearly intimated that I thought the allegation was absurd.

The attorney chimed in. "He claims you have completely mishandled his daughter's treatment."

"Based on what?

"They claim she has lost hearing."

"Has she?" I asked. The attorney said nothing, but the Chief nodded. "I'm really sorry about that. Really, I am."

"Why did you use Kanamycin?"

"Because it was the only antibiotic her infection was sensitive to. She knew the risk. We developed a course of action that saved her life."

"Regardless, our firm has been notified that you have been named in a malpractice suit. Her father is suing you and the manufacturer of Kanamycin."

I had no reaction. Frankly, I was numb. The rest of the day was a blur. I believed in my heart that I had done the right thing, the best I could for my patient. I adhered to all the standards of medical care. I saved the life of this person who unquestionably would have died had I not intervened. But because of an unfortunate secondary outcome of treatment, I was held personally responsible for the complication.

Near eleven o'clock that night an automobile came to a stop in front of our home, a most unusual event in our neighborhood. A man got out, walked up to the front door, and rang the bell. I answered it.

"Dr. Keyloun?" the man asked.

"Yes."

"This is for you." He handed me a folded envelope. I opened it. It was a subpoena.

"You have a lot of goddamned nerve coming to my home in the dead of night!" I hissed.

"I know," said the process server, "I'm sorry. I had to take this as a part-time job, because I need the extra money to help put my son through medical school."

I was mute standing in the doorway in my pajamas. I vacillated between punching him in the nose and erupting in laughter.

Ultimately, the insurance company settled with the claimant. It was, to them, a nuisance lawsuit. From a financial perspective, it was not worth their time or energy to go to trial, so they simply made a payment that made the claimants happy. Did the compensation really offset the hardship of her hearing loss? I will never know, but a few weeks after the settlement was made and paperwork completed, my former patient reached out to me. She wanted to know if I would still be her doctor!

I felt like a duck in an arcade shooting gallery. I had already been shot down once; there was no way I was about to pop back up for her to aim at me again. There was no way I could continue to care for her. It was clear to me that malpractice litigation was emerging as a quick fix for financial gain, regardless of its merits. On further reflection, I realized that her lawsuit was part of an escalating trend epitomized by one, celebrated lawsuit.

In the late seventies, a local newspaper ran a photograph of an "egregious" medical offense on its front page. A woman had gone to a plastic surgeon for a panniculectomy, a "tummy tuck." It was not trivial cosmetic surgery. Decades before the invention of liposuction, a panniculectomy was an invasive procedure requiring multiple incisions to remove excess skin and belly fat. But for this patient, her protuberant abdomen was a source of extreme anxiety, and she implored the plastic surgeon to fix it. After surgery was completed, her navel was displaced two inches off center. This was the photo the newspaper ran: her bare, post-surgical abdomen. To the casual observer, given the number of incisions and scars, the position of her navel was hardly noticeable. But she complained that the asymmetry compounded her anxiety, and her navel was subsequently replaced to its rightful position in the middle of her abdomen.

Even so, she sued, claiming mental and emotional anguish.

One might think this was a frivolous lawsuit, one that had little merit, considering the triviality of the complaint relative to the enormity of her surgery, not to mention the fact that it had been quickly repaired without incident. Nonetheless, she won her case, and she was awarded $854,000.

In my opinion, this case opened the floodgates of malpractice lawsuits. At least, it seemed to do so in New York. To millions who read the paper, it was like the buzzer at the starting gate at a racetrack: *If she could get that kind of money for a displaced belly button, then I've got to find myself a malpractice attorney!*

Back when I entered private practice, Mutual of Wausau, the principal underwriter of malpractice insurance in New York State, abdicated. They discontinued writing policies for physicians, no matter how pristine their record or status in the profession. Another company, Argonaut, stepped in to fill the void, but after several years, they, too, abandoned the State of New York. Both companies cited the escalation in the number of claims and the outrageous awards handed down by juries as the reasoning behind their withdrawal.

In 1975 the New York State Medical Society came to the rescue by creating the Medical Liability Mutual Insurance Company. Every physician practicing in the state of New York was obligated to deposit several thousand dollars into a treasury, in order to fund a reserve that met the legal requirements of the insurance industry. It has maintained solvency mainly because it assiduously defends its membership against trivial and egregious claims. However, premiums continue to escalate unabated.

A young married man worked for Consolidated Edison, the principal utility company serving New York City. He was on the job one day, and was instructed to carry two buckets of gasoline to a work site. At some point, he elected to take a break. He set down the two canisters and lit a cigarette. He and the canisters of gas went up in flames. He was transported to St. Vincent's Hospital, where he came under the care Don Weinstein, a very competent plastic surgeon.

The patient had suffered second- and third-degree burns over fifty-five percent of his body. The extent of the burn was clearly life threatening, and I was called in consultation to be certain that no medical problem interfered with his treatment or convalescence. He was given the standards of care for such an injury: fluids, blood, antibiotics, ointments, and analgesics. He survived the initial trauma, but required many skin grafts. Don treated him as if he were his own son, and performed the grafts with exceptional skill. The patient spent almost eight weeks convalescing in the hospital before he was finally ready for discharge.

The night before he was to go home, he went to the bathroom and collapsed with cardiac arrest. Heroic efforts were made to resuscitate him, but after considerable time had elapsed, he was ultimately pronounced dead.

The autopsy revealed that he died of a massive pulmonary embolus. A clot somewhere in his abdomen or leg dislodged and plugged the flow of blood in the artery leading to his lung. It was a gut-wrenching tragedy that no one could have predicted. He had never once had complained of discomfort in his legs or difficulty breathing.

His distraught wife sued Con Ed. Her claim (through her lawyer) was that her husband had not been properly trained. She alleged the company neglected to teach him how to transport gasoline. Common sense dictates that a match should never be lit anywhere near a volatile flammable liquid, but the young widow was a tragic figure, and the case moved forward.

Con Ed (ironically not the widow) sued for wrongful death. To cast the widest net they could (to ensnare as many doctors as they could, thus maximizing the money available for a judgment), they named the plastic surgeon, the hospital, me and anyone else whose name appeared in the patient's chart. It was their claim that we, not his injuries, were liable for his death. They claimed that it was our obligation to not only care for his burns, but also to keep him alive at all costs.

Don Weinstein was emotionally devastated. I, however, was rather sanguine. The man had received the best care imaginable. I knew in my heart that malpractice hadn't been committed, so I believed we would prevail. As the case approached trial, Con Ed settled with the wife, and all claims against the doctors and hospital were dismissed. The fact was that the patient's injury fell under the worker's compensation statute. We all breathed a heavy sigh of relief.

Subsequent to this case, Don attempted to insulate himself from liability by calling in a myriad of consultants for every burn case he treated. He had an army of doctors see his patients: hematologists, pulmonary specialists, and rehabilitation specialists. He ordered mechanical compressive bandages for his patient's legs. He went so far as to call in dieticians to design and prepare custom meals. He left no door opened through which a malpractice attorney could enter to claim that not all that could have been done had been done. Did it reduce mortality? That's difficult to prove. Did it raise the cost of treating burns? Exponentially. It's called defensive medicine, and it has become commonplace.

In an attempt to insulate themselves from malpractice claims, physicians engage in practices that seem excessive at first blush. Ordering MRI tests on simple sprains, requesting C-T scans for a headache, blood tests for a runny nose, and prescribing antibiotics for the common cold represent a spectrum of behavior that is designed to insulate oneself from scrutiny and malpractice. The cost of such behavior is enormous, and it is ultimately passed on to the consumer in the manner of increased insurance premiums. But short of legislation to protect doctors from frivolous lawsuits, there is no way to modify such behavior.

Physicians, in turn, are being subjected to insurance premiums that increase exponentially every year. The cost has gotten to the point that many physicians can no longer afford to maintain a solo private practice, so instead they seek employment in hospital complexes or group practices. Having been named in a number of lawsuits, I witnessed firsthand the insanity of tort litigation.

One day, after I had just finished with a patient, I walked through a packed waiting area to hand Rose the patient's chart. A man unfamiliar to me was seated on one of the couches. He had disheveled grey hair, was wearing rumpled pants and a filthy wrinkled shirt, and he clutched a tattered briefcase as if it were a life preserver. Upon seeing me, he stood and approached me.

"Are you Dr. Keyloun?" he asked.

What a silly question, I thought. *Who else would I be in this small office, wearing a lab coat and holding a stethoscope, when there is only one name on the door?*

"Yes, I'm Dr. Keyloun," I said.

He pulled an envelope from the briefcase, handed it to me, and in front of a room full of patients announced, "You've been served."

Rose bolted from her chair behind her desk, and with menace in her eyes chased the man from the office, yelling, "Get out of here, you son of a bitch!" He scurried out the door like a cockroach.

It was clearly a tactic to humiliate and demean me in front of my patients. I looked around the room, half expecting to see accusatory glares of assent from them. Instead, I saw a room full of stunned and horrified faces. Even holding a lawsuit in my hands, my heart swelled at how my patients instantly rallied around me against the egregious slap in the face I had just been given.

"Will you excuse me for a moment?" I asked the room at large. Rose and I retreated to my consultation room together, where we opened the envelope to learn the details of the claim. When she saw the name of the claimant, Rose got really angry. She knew the patient in question from the neighborhood and knew that I had meticulously and thoroughly cared for her.

The case was ultimately dismissed, but the damage was done. Frivolous lawsuits were increasingly more common, and worse, their pursuit seemed to reach new levels of malevolence. With each passing day, I believed more strongly that people (and their lawyers) viewed malpractice like a game; doctors were merely potential sources of untold revenue. I never thought I'd have those beliefs confirmed so definitively in my own home one evening over dinner.

Suburbia is a pleasant place to live. Our home was on a quiet *cul de sac*, but there was not one child nearby for our son to play with. We were far removed from a neighborhood like the one I grew up in Brooklyn, which was teeming with children of all ages and stripes. Carol and I joined a country club both to expand our social net within our new community and to find playmates for our son. One of the members of our country club was a personal injury attorney. A pleasant guy, Fred Paolini was very open about what he did for a living, and frequently regaled us with stories of his exploits. Most involved suing the City of New York for injuries resulting from potholes, cracked sidewalks, or subway mishaps. However, he also engaged in malpractice suits.

Carol and I decided to have some friends over for dinner. Seated at our table were the Paolinis and our dear friends John and Barbara. John was an Ob/Gyn we knew from St. Vincent's, who had moved to our neighborhood a year before we did. To round out the table, Carol invited a woman whom she recently befriended at a charity event. We had no idea that her husband Stavros was also a malpractice attorney. Stavros became visibly excited when he was introduced to Fred, who was clearly a giant in his industry, and one on whom Stavros wanted to make an impression. They immediately began to talk shop, and after several glasses of wine, Fred became quite expansive. He told stories how he hired consultants to dress his clients in such a way as to gain jury sympathy, how he coached clients to walk in a particular manner to reinforce the claimed injury, even how to emotionally respond to testimony from the defense witnesses. It was all staged. It was Courtroom Theater. Stavros sucked it all in like a dry sponge.

Fred was proud to say that he even hired recruiters. His law firm engaged people who worked in the record departments of large hospitals, and enticed them with favors and money to refer potential cases. These employees were asked to flag the hospital charts of difficult births or of children that might have suffered brain damage, as these were richly rewarding tort cases. In many instances the parents were unaware they had a claim, until a visit from one of the attorneys or paralegals in the firm convinced them otherwise.

"It doesn't matter how good the medical care was," Fred conspired with Stavros, "there is no way to defend a claim of injury to a child, even a congenital problem. The sight of a maimed kid in a courtroom is a slam dunk."

"You think it's all a joke," John said through clenched teeth.

"Look, it's nothing personal," Fred replied, as he dove into the dessert laid before him. "I don't hate doctors. Doctors are my best friends! Look at me, I'm having dinner at a table with two of them," he chuckled affably.

I caught a glimpse of John quietly seething at the end of the table.

"It's like this," Fred continued, "each case is like a key to a locked vault where insurance companies deposit all their premiums. It's my job to find the right key to open the vault."

His last comment was like a knife in my belly. I had tried to be the good host, but my ire got the better of me, and I quipped, "I guess you've found lots of keys, Fred." I went on, "Who do you think fills that vault? It's because of guys like you why my malpractice premium keeps going up! You must know that there are two insurance companies that have stopped writing malpractice policies altogether."

Fred simply dove further into his dessert, while Stavros stared at him, panting like an eager puppy awaiting more treats. Thinking the horribly awkward conversation had been quashed, we all quietly returned to the remainder of our meals.

Without warning, and as if nothing else had been said, Fred leaned in to Stavros. "A woman was driving her car—one of those new ones, they look like off-road vehicles—when it lost all power and came to a sudden, dead stop on the highway. The guy behind her never saw any brake lights, and plowed right into her. She was fine—a little shaken, maybe—but the guy suffered a horrible fracture to his knee."

Stavros leaned back, and anticipating the next sentence, said, "So you represented the guy? To get around no-fault?"

"Hell no! I represented the gal. I sued the car company."

"But he hit her."

"But the car company has deeper pockets than his insurance! I sent her to physical therapy for a year, and I had her see a shrink for seven months. Then, at trial, I got experts to testify that faulty wiring caused her car to die. It was one of my best wins." He looked up at the rest of us. "I won a lot of money for Suzanne Deutsch," he said with a smirk, and winking to Stavros added, "and damn near paid off the mortgage on my house in East Hampton in the process."

A silence fell over the table, as it registered with each of us listening that Fred had just betrayed his client's confidence. Illegal and unethical in its own right, the affront was made all the worse because Suzanne Deutsch was a dear friend.

John became totally unglued. We had all sat at the table, politely nodding and gritting our teeth, all the while listening to this huckster detail with pride how he worked to get the most out of the system for his clients, ignoring or dismissing any consequence to the individuals he targeted. It was easier not to engage. But to John, this was the last straw.

"You two are lower than snakes!" he screamed. "Who the hell do you think you are, screwing around with peoples lives like that?" John was a consummate, caring doctor, and his outburst was so atypical for the mild mannered man he normally was. He stood at the table, eyes wide and face flushed. "I just spent a week in court, defending myself from an outrageous lawsuit. And it was shitheads like you that made my life miserable!"

"John," Fred tried to backpedal, "John, you're taking it too personally. It's not. I promise."

"You're full of shit! You're in it for the money, consequences be damned! You can all go to hell!"

John stormed out of the dining room into the living room. It was as far away as he could get, short of leaving the house. It was an embarrassing scene, but I can't say I blamed him, or disagreed with him. Carol played peacemaker and eventually managed to calm everyone down. And in the light of a new day, I found it very interesting to have been privy to the mindset and *modus operandi* of at least one very successful malpractice attorney.

I was not entirely saddened to learn, years later, that Fred had been sued under the RICO law, the law originally enacted to capture the ill-gotten gains of organized crime. As details of the criminal case against him spread through our town and country club, we came to learn that not all of Fred's "recruitment" dealings were on the up and up. The State had built a case against him for, among other things, witnesses tampering. Fred got caught when one of his witnesses, who had testified that he had seen a particular accident, was actually incarcerated at the time of the incident. Fred was found guilty, and the government attached all of his possessions. Fred lost his license and went to jail.

I hate to admit to *schadenfreude*, but I quietly considered it a win for the doctors.

Walking Away

There is something surreal about moving out. A person can spend so many years in a given place that it seems to become a living, breathing entity in its own right. It has its own character, quirks and personality. It becomes an inextricable part of a person's identity, reflected in the furnishings, décor or personal effects dotted about. But then something happens, or a decision is made, and the person must separate himself from his space. Bit by bit, its contents get dismantled, disassembled, and removed, until nothing is left but the bare walls. Suddenly, those walls look dirtier, the rooms look smaller, and the space is cold and lifeless. It feels like something has died, and there is no escaping a profound sense of loss.

I stood in the empty room that used to be my waiting area, staring through the secretary's window, past the empty filing cabinets, and out the circular-framed windows of the Maritime Building onto Seventh Avenue. I had worked in this comfortable suite of offices for upwards of ten years. I had made a life in this place, a wonderful, challenging, frustrating, joyous career here, and now I was leaving it all behind.

My decision to leave was not impulsive. With each passing year, I was becoming more and more disenchanted, not with the practice of medicine, but with what practicing medicine had become.

For me, the changes began early in my career, with the advent of Medicare. At its inception, Medicare was a boon for both patient and physician, and most everyone was pleasantly surprised by the efficiency of the system. However, the very first patient who entered my office with a Medicare card presaged the future. In order to be reimbursed, I needed only complete a one-page document. Form 1492 required a signature to verify service and diagnosis. However, the line to which I was to sign my name was not labeled "Physician" or "Doctor," but rather "Vendor." So, too, was the label "Patient" replaced by the word "Client." To many, it was an innocuous change, meant only to make the form more universal, so that suppliers of medical equipment or medical paraphernalia could use the same document. To others, like myself, it was a deliberate debasement of a physician's status. A simple change in nomenclature reduced physicians' influence and prestige, and redefined us as merchants.

I had not studied for as long and as hard as I did, I had not trained as diligently as I had, so that I could work as a merchant "selling" treatment to "clients." I was a Doctor. I chose Medicine as a career because I believed it was a noble endeavor to care for people. I could easily have joined my father's business in the garment industry, but was turned off by the dog-eat-dog environment, the hucksters, bribery, and grubby dealings.

I would be naïve to say that the administration of medical care is not a business. But the business of medical care cannot be equated with the retail market. In the retail market, buyers choose and purchase exactly what they want. The business of medicine depends on what service is being offered and how it is presented. And all around me, whether institutionally or individually, it seemed that what was being offered was not necessarily that which was in the best interest of the patient, but that which resulted in the greatest profit.

Prior to the implementation of Medicare, insurance companies wrote indemnity policies that reimbursed a doctor's fee and cost of hospital care. Medicare brought with it a new concept. No longer did physicians and institutions determine the cost of service. Medicare set its reimbursement schedule based on what it deemed to be the "prevailing rate" of that service (ostensibly, a regional average cost). Medicare was the sole arbiter of the prevailing rate, and was solely responsible for adjusting it. Other insurance providers that wrote medical policies were quick to follow the Medicare lead to set and maintain prevailing rates for medical procedures. Very quickly, doctors were forced to either accept the payment terms of the insurance companies, or require their patients to pay entirely out of pocket. Few could afford to do so.

With increased power came increased competition, and insurers began to focus on increasing market share. A representative from Blue Cross/ Blue Shield came to my office one day and presented me with a proposition: if I joined their system and accepted their fee structure, they would send me an unlimited number of patients. During the entirety of his presentation, there wasn't a single mention of the welfare of the insured patients; the proposal was merely an effort to maximize their profit margin. People had become a commodity.

I already had all the patients I could possibly care for and needed no more, so I passed on the offer. But the younger physicians who were just starting practice, who weren't established and who had not yet developed a following, were seduced by the enticement. It was a bargain with the devil. Eventually, the insurance companies universally ratcheted down their fee schedules to cut costs, and physicians in their network had no alternative but to accept them.

Trapped by the limits of the insurance companies, physicians were forced to find ways of generating income. Given that there are only so many hours in a day to see patients in an office setting, and considering how many more billable services are available in a hospital environment, physicians began to seize every opportunity to hospitalize their patients. Hosts of unnecessary tests and procedures were ordered. The hospitals were only too happy to comply. They, after all, were merchants, too.

At St. Vincent's, the Sisters of Charity were dedicated to caring for the sick. However, they were also saddled with the reality of maintaining the financial solvency of the hospital. Prior to Medicare, indigent patients were cared for in voluntary hospitals that billed local government a per diem capitated fee. Once Medicare's methods of reimbursement were in play, the hospital tried to maximize income by "unbundling" its services, and billing for each service separately. Taken to its extreme, they would charge for an aspirin tablet, and charge separately for its delivery to the patient.

Hospitals hired salaried physicians to care for the patients in their institutions, and billed Medicare and insurance carriers in their name. No longer could a neighborhood doctor admit and care for his or her own patient. Once patients entered the hospital, they came under the purview of the "hospitalist," a doctor who the patient often didn't know, and who was rarely incentivized to work beyond the hours of a prescribed workday.

Additionally, advisors determined that there was an asset value to large, successful practices. They reasoned that if hospitals could purchase these practices from retiring physicians, they would be turned over to a doctor on the hospital's salary, thereby guaranteeing the patients remained within the hospital's system. Practices were viewed as products with monetary value that could be bartered, sold or depreciated. There was no regard for the individual people involved, many of whom quickly soured on their newly assigned physician, and found their own doctor elsewhere. Since the relationship that had originally nurtured the practice no longer existed, more often than not these purchased practices quickly dissolved.

Financial "experts" determined that costs could be further wrung from the system if hospitals had more bargaining power with their suppliers, including the pharmaceutical companies. Thus began the merger of hospitals into networks. With ever-expanding networks' bureaucracy, the intimacy with patients declined even further.

The insanity of the way medical care was degenerating could not be better exemplified than by the plight of Simon Greenbaum. Simon was a patient of mine whom I had diagnosed with breast cancer. Such cancer in men is unusual, but not unprecedented. After several other doctors had dismissed the lump in his chest as "nothing serious," I saw Simon through a mastectomy, radiation treatment and chemotherapy. He came through like a champ, and as far as we knew, he was completely cancer-free.

He was thereafter a devoted patient. One day he came to my office unannounced, clutching his chest and perspiring as if he were in a sauna. He could barely walk. He staggered into my office and leaned against the doorjamb.

"Simon, what's the matter?" I asked, alarmed.

"My chest hurts."

"Why didn't you go straight to the hospital?"

"You're the only person I trust."

Good God, I thought, *that kind of trust can be your own undoing.*

I took Simon to an examining room in which a patient was already waiting for me. When he saw the state that Simon was in, he was all too happy to oblige as I politely shooed him back to the waiting room. I hooked Simon up to an electrocardiogram as fast as I could. Sure enough, the results screamed "HEART ATTACK!"

There was little I could do for him in my office. We were not equipped to start an intravenous drip or to administer narcotics. Nor did we store oxygen tanks. I left Simon hooked up to the EKG, rushed to the telephone, and called the St. Vincent's emergency room, conveniently located diagonally across the street.

They refused to send an ambulance or a gurney to bring Simon to the hospital.

"You need to call the police, Doctor. They will call for the ambulance."

"But I'm an attending physician," I pleaded. "My office is just across the street in your outpatient clinic building. Your ambulances are parked right outside my front door!"

"I'm sorry, Doctor, but we have a protocol." *Click.*

I called 911, and waited. I could have called for a private ambulance, but that certainly would have taken many hours, time that Simon did not have. While my patient lay on the examining table, I nervously fidgeted over the EKG, praying that the erratic scratches on the tape didn't devolve into anything worse before help arrived. He could experience a fatal arrhythmia at any moment, and there would be nothing I could do about it. Rose, meanwhile, was calling everyone she knew at St. Vincent's to alert them that a heart attack patient was on his way.

The police arrived after a considerable delay. When they saw the chaos in my office, they finally called for an ambulance. One was dispatched—not from St. Vincent's, but from Roosevelt Hospital, two miles north! As the EMTs lifted Simon into the back of the vehicle, I growled to the ambulance driver, "If you take him uptown to Roosevelt, he could die on the way. Do that, and I'll make your life a living hell. You think I don't know the game you're playing, trying to poach this patient?"

Breathless, Simon raised a finger at the driver, struggled to wag it, and pointed towards the St. Vincent's ambulance bay fifty yards away. There he was taken, and there at St. Vincent's is where he recovered.

The incident was so dispiriting to me. It was as if the only thing anyone saw in Mr. Greenbaum was a dollar value tattooed across his forehead. All anyone had to do to cash in on it was to snatch the patient. Finders, keepers. It didn't matter that I was his doctor, that Roosevelt was not my hospital, or that my hospital was so close as to make the debate ridiculous. There was money to be made in Simon Greenbaum.

I learned later that St. Vincent's refused to send an ambulance for fear of liability. The threat of malpractice extended far beyond individual physician's practices. The police were the only ones authorized to call for a city ambulance. Had St. Vincent's sent one, and had Simon died during transport, the hospital could have been held accountable, because the transport had been "unauthorized." Never mind the irrational mandate that disallowed a hospital to dispatch its own emergency crews; the fact that the hospital was willing to jeopardize the life of a patient in crisis in order to avoid a potential issue of liability seemed anathema for an institution dedicated to healthcare.

Beyond the institutional nonsense, saddest of all was observing how this "anything for a profit" culture affected the day-to-day dealings with my colleagues. For a time, I held the title Chairman of the Peer Review Committee. It was mostly a hollow title, as it carried no authority to bring anyone before an ethics committee or to sanction individual's behavior. My influence was limited to moral persuasion. However, being on the peer review committee allowed me to observe how others practiced. It wasn't always a pleasant sight.

I was in the dialysis unit one morning, when an orderly wheeled in a gurney. Lying on it corpse-like was a ninety-two year old patient. His lifeless eyes were sunk deep within their hollow sockets and stared blankly from behind a gaunt, sallow complexion. Resting on the thin sheet that covered him, his emaciated arms were bones wrapped in tissue paper skin that was mottled with countless blood blisters.

I looked to the head nurse and asked, "Why is this gentleman here?"

"He's scheduled for dialysis, Doctor," she replied, her expression clearly asking, *Why else would he be here?*

Summoning my status as Chair, I retrieved the patient's chart (something I would have had no authority to do in normal circumstances). The man had cancer of his urinary bladder. The disease was so extensive that it had strangled both ureters. The obstruction of the tubes allowed such little urine to pass from his kidneys to his bladder that the man had become uremic. It was a hopeless situation. He had terminal cancer, and at ninety two years of age, there was no long term benefit to start him on a dialysis regime. I could only imagine how this patient's physician, Dr. Gremline, had sold the idea of dialysis to his family.

"Your father is very sick. The cancer is preventing him from expelling urine, and he is at a critical point right now. It will kill him. However, we have a simple machine that can clean his blood of poisons. Dialysis will keep him alive."

What grieving son or daughter wouldn't send their ailing parent for dialysis under these circumstances? But, while all the information presented to them was factual, it was by no means complete. The very same case could have been presented in a very different way.

"Your father has a cancer that cannot be removed surgically, and there is no effective treatment for it. If we do nothing, he will lapse into a painless coma and pass away peacefully. But I want you to know that there is the option for dialysis, which would cleanse his blood of poisons. I can't tell you how much longer it will allow him to live, but I do know that he will experience much more pain from the cancer."

This is an equally factual way of presenting this man's case, and in my opinion, far more accurate. I doubted that it had been presented to the patient's family in such a fashion, and I questioned Dr. Gremline's motives for not being completely forthright.

When Gremline arrived on the unit, I asked if he would step outside for a chat. I directed him to the stairwell landing, behind a heavy steel door so that no one might overhear our conversation.

"What the hell are you doing to that poor man?" I asked.

"He has every right to live longer," Gremline replied with an air of haughtiness.

"Longer? He's nearly a hundred years old with end-stage bladder cancer! How much longer can he possibly have?"

"It's not for me to say, Dr. Keyloun." Gremline continued with added righteous indignation, "I am providing him with the best care available."

"So instead of allowing him to die peacefully in uremic coma, your idea of 'the best care' is to keep him alive long enough for him to die in excruciating pain?"

Gremline just stared at me without saying a word.

"You're fucking pathetic." My voice was thick with disappointment and disgust.

I knew his motives were mercenary. Subjecting a dying man to dialysis purely for the added income was downright unethical in my mind, but I had no recourse. Medicare would never question the validity of his diagnosis, nor the legitimacy of the procedure, and the hospital was happy for the income.

It was like this everywhere I turned. Every new scientific advance seemed to have bred an industry. In 1960, dialysis was merely a medical-center curiosity reserved for treating patients who overdosed a medication or ingested a toxic chemical. It wasn't until 1973 that Medicare undertook the reimbursement for treating end-stage renal disease. And with that validation, it became a money-making venture unto itself.

When Magnetic Resonance Imaging came onto the scene, we all marveled at the new technology. Anatomical structures appeared clearer than ever before, even more so than in an operating room or at an autopsy table. An MRI surpassed older diagnostic modalities in revealing unseen (and unimagined) disease and injury. The MRI was a wonder of science.

And it didn't take long for its use to be corrupted.

I had a patient, an older gentleman, who came in complaining of a sore ankle. I examined him, and found nothing out of the ordinary. There was no limitation of motion, it was not swollen, nor was it tender to the touch. Ordinarily, I would have prescribed an analgesic, warm soaks and rest. Only had that prescription failed would I have pursued his complaint further. But my patient preempted me.

"Well, Doc, how about you send me for an MRI?"

"Not yet. Let's see how you do on medicine and rest, first. Besides an MRI is rather expensive."

"Why do you care, Doc?" he replied. "Insurance is paying for it."

No! I wanted to scream. *We are all paying for it!*

As its publicity and popularity grew, more patients demanded an MRI, even for trivial complaints. Physicians obliged; no doctor in his right mind refused a patient's request, for fear that a missed diagnosis would result in a lawsuit. Likewise, as society became increasingly litigious, doctors began to include MRIs as a part of their defensive medical strategy. The result was an overwhelming demand for the technology.

A business opportunity was born. The image that an MRI machine produces is generated by radio waves passed through a magnetic field. Because the machine utilizes no radiation (as do X-rays or C-T scans), one need not be a doctor or hospital to own one. Individuals and consortia purchased machines and ran them as for-profit businesses. At one time, there were more MRI machines within a one-quarter mile radius of our suburban town than there were in all of Canada. Demand influenced supply. The insurance companies never questioned the necessity for an MRI, they simply paid the bill, and passed the skyrocketing costs on to their subscribers in the form of increased premiums.

To me, however, the most bewildering industry of our time is the expansion of interventions for coronary artery disease. Penicillin virtually eradicated rheumatic fever, which meant the disappearance of rheumatic heart disease. Open heart surgery to replace a diseased, damaged mitral valve all but vanished. As this reservoir of patients was exhausted, a new surgical specialty came to the fore: coronary bypass. With the newfound ability to arrest and restore the beating heart, vascular surgeons were able to bypass any clogged coronary artery with a vein removed from the patient's leg.

When the surgery was first performed in 1968, the initial success was remarkable. Patients with uncompromising angina were symptom-free overnight, convalescence in the hospital was mere days, and most patients embarked on supervised exercise programs soon afterward. The procedure, however, was not without its own complications. Often, the bypass graft itself clogged within several years. A wave of pharmaceutical products—mostly blood thinners and anti-platelets compounds—were developed to forestall the complication.

Meanwhile, cardiologists discovered that they could introduce a catheter with a balloon at its tip through an artery in the groin to the point of narrowing, and by inflating the balloon, they could break up the plaque that was preventing the free flow of blood in the coronary artery. Balloon angioplasty was first performed in 1977, with results as effective as open-heart surgery. However, the procedure brought with it newfound complications: sometimes the artery collapsed soon after the procedure, leading to a massive heart attack, and sometimes patients developed restenosis, a condition where scar tissue develops and reclogs the artery. Eventually it was discovered that a metal mesh, called a stent, could be expanded within a coronary artery to maintain its patency.

There is no question that these techniques of coronary intervention have saved countless lives. But, like everything else, they were corruptible. Cardiologists found a new source of income, and were eager to capitalize on it. When hospitals learned how generous was the reimbursement, they spent a fortune constructing new catheterization labs, assuming the state-of-the-art facilities would attract more patients. Hospital administrators became consumed with keeping these new labs occupied and functioning in order to amortize their cost.

Cardiac surgeons who had exhausted the reservoir of rheumatic valvular disease adopted bypass surgery with a passion. It seemed to me that anyone with chest pain remotely referable to the heart underwent a catheterization procedure and coronary angiography. One can only speculate on how many patients underwent angioplasty for only marginally narrowed coronary arteries.

Like many other discoveries before it, coronary care became an industry unto itself. Competing providers waged a fierce battle for market share with ever newer procedures, devices and methods of deployment entering the marketplace. I had no way of knowing that, in the decades since these procedures became commonplace, years of voluminous statistics show that they do not prolong life. In fact, there are now articles in the medical literature confirming that dementia is a long-term complication of coronary artery bypass grafting. There is undeniable proof that spending billions of dollars on surgery is, in many cases, no better than good medical care, diet, and appropriate medicine. At the time, all I could see was the apparent feeding frenzy, and it bewildered me.

The practice of medicine had changed. It had become something unrecognizable to me, to what I had envisioned my life to be. Coupled with the omnipresent, looming specter of malpractice, I began to find the reasons for my unease, my distaste, my unhappiness in the profession I once loved. To continue to practice in this ever-mutating environment necessarily meant allowing myself to become a tiny cog in a monolithic machine. I had already stood against accepting such a role early in my career—in fact, before I even had a career—when I refused the full-time employment offer from St. Vincent's in lieu of the risk of private practice. That same entrepreneurial spirit with which I was raised refused to allow me to succumb.

I had initially pursued Medicine believing it was a profession dedicated to service. Yes, it was possible (even likely) to earn a very good living, but caring for people was at its core. We made decisions based on the best interest of the patient, and little more. Sure, there were rivalries and petty jealousies, and there was no shortage of unscrupulous characters. But there was also camaraderie and a unity in the medical profession. In the twenty or so years since I graduated medical school, I witnessed the slow dissolution of that unity, I saw the doctor-patient relationship become less personal and more adversarial, I watched as executives at insurance companies dictated standards (and costs) of care, I observed the insanity of defensive medicine, and I felt the sting when my and my colleagues' competence was challenged not by peer review, but by tort law. I witnessed unnecessary hospitalizations and watched doctors perform outrageous procedures with the tacit approval of hospital administration. Worst of all, I watched helplessly as Medicine morphed from the care-based profession that I loved to a profit-driven industry of which I wanted no part. It was a course I no longer wished to travel. If I was to be considered a merchant, I rather have earned my keep in the business arena. Medicine should never have succumbed to the marketplace. Its nobility is diminished.

It took over two years to dismantle my practice. I stopped accepting new patients. Then, one by one, as patients came for their check ups, I referred them to colleagues who were specialists. Heart patients were sent to cardiologists, bowel disorders to gastroenterologists, and rheumatic diseases to rheumatologists. All my dialysis patients were transferred to the care of the Chief of Nephrology.

I told patients that I was retiring from practice. Some understood my decision, others were incredulous. Almost every time, my announcement was met with tears. "But, you're too young!" they lamented. I loved my patients, and they loved me in return. To cause this disruption in my patients' lives made my heart ache.

Above all, I felt terribly for Rose. She helped me to methodically dismantle my practice, all the while watching her job, one that she dearly loved, slowly evaporate before her eyes. Over the years, I had allowed her to assume enormous responsibility, and she accepted it admirably. No letter of reference could ever convey all that she did for me, or all that she was capable of doing. I wondered about her future, if she would ever be employed by anyone who would allow her to flourish the way I though she should.

With every passing month, the number of patients in my office grew fewer and fewer. I no longer made rounds in the hospital. I continued to attend conferences, because I still wanted to learn, to keep abreast. But it became painful. I began to feel like an outsider. My colleagues all knew I was leaving. I don't recall if any wished me well.

My patients, however, were effusive. Letters poured in, each telling me how much I would be missed. I could not bring myself to read them in the office. Each envelope that Rose brought to my desk was quickly placed in my briefcase to be brought home and read quietly and privately on my sun porch.

Toward the end, I felt like I was walking under water. Every motion was a struggle. Everything before me was enveloped in a fog, unclear, unsure. Every good-bye was like death itself. I had built a wonderful practice over the years, and had established an honorable reputation, and now it was coming to an end.

I left the office that last day with a heavy heart. Standing in the doorway, on the threshold between past and future, I had a sudden fear that I would never find anything more satisfying than caring for another human being and doing a good job of it. I had secured a future for myself, but was I making the right decision? Was my reaction to the frustrations of medical practice appropriate? Had I done enough?

I shut my eyes, took a deep breath, and knowing in my heart that I had done some good, closed the door behind me.

Carol

It is difficult to reflect on one's career and not experience a touch of nostalgia. I thought we were living on the cutting edge of science during my years of practice, but in the intervening years since I left, the advances in medicine have been astonishing. More precise diagnoses and unprecedented treatments are possible because of the marvels of digital technology. There are now targeted medicines for the treatment of cancer and cures for certain types of leukemia. The unraveling of the human genome has opened vistas of opportunity to modify diseases that once were considered incurable.

I never imagined that someone so close to me as my wife would ever have had to rely on such advances. We were lucky insofar as I had come from the very field on which Carol's life would depend. I knew what to research, I knew what questions to ask, I knew some of the players involved. Perhaps most importantly, I had earned enough money that made it all possible for us to do it.

The results of her brain surgery were miraculous, if imperfect. Within weeks of having her neurostimulators activated, Carol suffered two major falls. The first occurred as she was straightening up the family room one night before dinner. Without warning, she pitched forward and hit her forehead on the coffee table, opening a seven-inch gash deep enough to expose bone.

"I went to put the remote on the TV, and the next thing I knew, I was on the floor and my head was bleeding," she explained. "I don't know what happened. I know I didn't trip on anything."

The second fall occurred a few weeks later, when some friends dropped her off after an afternoon lunching together. As she closed the front door to our home, I saw Carol topple backwards like a felled tree, banging the back of her head squarely on a door frame. Her knees never buckled, and she never attempted to break the fall. It was as if her brain didn't even register that she was falling.

Luckily, neither event resulted in permanent injury (I would have sworn she had cracked her skull that day by the sound it made when her head hit the wall). Although MRI scans revealed no bleeding or disruption of the probes, the falls indicated that there was something definitely wrong with her physiology, and within a couple of months of brain surgery, Carol began to lose her ability to walk. The doctors couldn't explain it. In a year, she was relegated again to her wheelchair.

Though it was a devastating setback, it is hard to argue that the brain surgery was "unsuccessful." Although Carol did not regain her ability to ambulate the way she might have hoped (or might have been led to believe she would), Deep Brain Stimulation has continued to do wonders for her tremor and rigidity. I am reminded just how dreadful her quality of life might have been every time I take her for a checkup, and her neurostimulators are temporarily turned off. The extent to which her tremor has progressed (and is still controlled) is alarming.

Setbacks and complications happen. They're unfortunate and unavoidable, and are no cause to blame anyone. What is truly lamentable to me, however, is the systematic loss of the doctor-patient relationship. There used to be a palpable bond between patient and doctor. People cared for each other, in the truest sense of the word. The indifference one encounters today is dispiriting. What we see now is very efficient and very mechanical, but it is also bland and impersonal, due largely to the increasing complexity and bureaucracy of practice. More time is spent sorting and entering data into electronic records than is spent with the patient. Doctors can and must see more patients in less time in order to satisfy the demands of the institutions they serve and the insurance carriers to whom they are beholden. There is ever less time in a doctor's office to just sit and chat with a patient. It is virtually impossible to survive in solo practice, so the remaining doctors in private practice are forced to either band together into groups, or work directly for hospitals. In fact, the number of physicians employed by hospitals exceeds that of those working privately. Even the institutions themselves have expanded, via mergers primarily, in order to compete. The intimacy of the doctor-patient relationship within these amorphous behemoth bureaucracies is almost non-existent.

Nurses are likewise burdened by regulations and paperwork. I remember the nurses at my hospital, and how they all seemed to be on a messianic mission. They were knowledgeable, efficient, dedicated, and above all, caring. There was little turnover. Some nurses spent their entire careers at St. Vincent's. It was most reassuring to know that your patients were left in their custody. Today, nurses are relegated to duties more akin to management, far removed from the patient. They are so busy entering data and filling out forms that little time remains for bedside care and nurturing support.

Still, I find it difficult to forgive when a night nurse is so inconvenienced by having to help Carol to the restroom after her second back surgery that she yells at her for not being able to walk fast enough.

"Walk, Missus! You have to walk! I'm not going to carry you!"

"I'm trying. It's the Parkinson's."

It is well understood that a nursing shortage exists in many institutions, but I find it equally inexcusable when a hospital nurse, sipping a soda in the nurse's station, merely shrugs and responds, "We're short-staffed" when I inquire as to why my convalescing wife had not been bathed in over four days.

Sick people are vulnerable. What they need is for their doctor to guide them through a trying and scary situation. But in today's system, there is no longer continuity of care. Private doctors relinquish care to hospitalist physicians whenever a patient is admitted. In group practices, patients can be seen by any one of the group members. Changes in insurance plans dictate whether or not patients can see the doctor they have come to know. In our case, it seems that every time I take Carol back to see one of her doctors, we are informed that he or she is no longer at that hospital, no longer in practice, or no longer a part of that specialty, and we are shepherded off to see someone new.

As good as they are, the lithium batteries that energize the neurostimulators wear out and need replacing. Carol's first set lasted for three and a half years. I called New York University Hospital and asked if Dr. McCarthy would be the doctor to replace them. I was told he no longer performed that kind of surgery.

Much had changed since Carol's DBS operation. Medicare had approved payment for deep brain surgery, so this (and all future related surgeries) would be covered by her policy. However, Medicare had also modified its participation rules. If a doctor accepted just one patient for what Medicare allowed, that doctor was then obligated to accept all patients for what Medicare allowed. It was all or none. In Dr. McCarthy's case, he declined to accept Medicare at all. He was in a position as Chief of Neurosurgery to demand full payment for his services, regardless of what any insurance policy reimbursed. Having had already spent an enormous sum of money on DBS when it was still experimental, now that the procedure was covered by Medicare, it didn't make sense for us to have Dr. McCarthy do the follow-up surgery for yet another out-of-pocket fee.

We were referred to a neurosurgeon in Valhalla, New York who turned out to have participated in Carol's original surgery while he had been the Chief Resident at New York University. Being a much younger man than Dr. McCarthy, I suspected it was he who used the metal clips in the race to close Carol's scalp incisions.

During her preoperative workup, I advised him that Carol had developed a severe allergy to adhesive tape, and to please only use hypoallergenic paper tape in the operating room. He and his nurse assistant both made notes of it in the chart. Carol went off to surgery, and I was called to pick her up around four o'clock in the afternoon. We were well into the hour-long drive back to our home when Carol turned to me and said, "Vic, my chest..."

"What about it?" I asked.

"It hurts."

It was not the crushing pain of a heart attack, nor the burning pain of indigestion. It was a severe itching, and she had a desperate need to scratch it.

"Please don't, Carol," I urged. "I'll look at it when we get home. We're almost there."

When I got her into the house, I helped her to remove her blouse, only to discover that the gauze over the incisions has been secured with a five-by-ten-inch sheet of adhesive tape! The skin adjacent to it was beet red, and I could see blisters forming under the adhesive bandage.

There was no alternative but to remove it. I peeled the tape away as gingerly as I could, but the blisters broke, exposing oozing, inflamed skin underneath. She looked like she had been scalded by hot water. Carol spent the next seven days with an angry, itchy rash across her chest, which required constant application of antibiotics and cortisone cream.

I was able to handle the problem, but I wondered, had I not been a doctor, what would I have done? I'm not certain a non-professional would have the temerity to take it upon himself to remove the tape. I couldn't image having to traipse the hour-long drive back to the hospital. I couldn't imagine how the wound would have looked after being exposed to the adhesive for hours.

More importantly, after having witnessed two individuals make separate notes about the allergy, I wondered how anyone could have made such an oversight. In Carol's case, it resulted in an unnecessary, painful inconvenience. But what if the allergy had been more serious?

When we returned to the hospital to have the surgical clips removed, the doctor marveled at the scabs still present on Carol's chest. I told him of the screw-up in his operating room. He did not apologize for the egregious lapse of communication, but he did say he would make a note of it.

Three and a half years passed too quickly before Carol required another replacement of her neurostimulators. We called the neurosurgeon in Valhalla, only to learn he transferred his practice to North Shore University Hospital, not three miles from our home. We thought it was a fortuitous turn of events. At our appointment, I politely reminded the doctor how Carol had suffered a severe allergic reaction to adhesive tape the last time, and I asked if he would take special care to use paper tape. He agreed and made a note in the chart in the presence of his operating room coordinator.

Carol's surgery was scheduled for ten o'clock the next morning. We arrived two hours early, as was prescribed, and waited to be called. It was noon when I approached the desk clerk.

"My wife was scheduled for ten. It's now noon. What is going on?"

She checked her computer. "Oh, no, sir. Your surgery was rescheduled yesterday for two o'clock this afternoon. Didn't anybody call you?"

"No. No, they did not."

There was no one in authority at whom I could scream, so we sat and waited. Carol was finally called in to surgery at three o'clock. We had been sitting in the waiting lounge since eight o'clock that morning.

If that was not insult enough, in the five-minute drive home from the hospital, Carol's chest began to burn. I examined her, and to my utter disbelief and consternation, found that they had once again used adhesive tape. Her chest was totally blistered. The pain was unimaginable. The carelessness was unimaginable. It was negligence pure and simple.

It is the indifference and the carelessness that I find bewildering. It pains me to witness the profession I so loved devolve into being "just a job" for so many. Of course, there are many wonderful caregivers in the world, and Carol and I have benefitted greatly by some of them. Dr. Stancic and his team at Beth Israel remain for us our gold standard, the bastion of professionalism. But the industry of Medicine—from the hospitals, to the pharmaceutical companies, insurance agencies, lawyers, doctors, nurses and staff—has become so suffocating that patient care is the first, and biggest, casualty.

Caring for a spouse with a chronic illness is never something one dreams about for his retirement (nor, I am sure, did Carol ever dream of being the ailing spouse). It is difficult to watch the one you love suffer, and I try to be as helpful and supportive as I can. For all we've been through, we continue to enjoy our lives. We trundle on. After all, what's the alternative?

Carol and I were looking through some old photos from early in our marriage. We came upon a series of pictures from a road trip we took upstate to visit my sister and brother-in-law. In one photo, Carol—young and devastatingly beautiful—stood beaming in front of the car with our infant son balanced on her hip.

"Oh, look at that," Carol said, brushing the picture with her fingertip, "I used to be quite a dish!" She paused, thought for a second, then looked at me with an affected shrug and added, "Now I'm just a plate!"

For as much as her disease has progressed, and for all the inconveniences and indignities it forces upon her, the fact that Carol has been able to maintain such an active sense of humor about it is a testament to her indomitable spirit.

I should tell her more often: she is still a dish to me.

I often reflect on times past, when life was simpler and the rewards of a medical practice seemed more tangible. From time to time, I sneak back to my little den in the small, one-level Levitt house to which Carol and I moved ten years ago. I rummage through the deep file drawer in my rolltop desk and find the small box of memorabilia I have stashed there. In it, tucked under my old stethoscope, are the letters I saved from my dear patients. As I read through them, I remember some of the best years of my life, and I think fondly of all those people who passed through it.

It has been nearly sixty years since I began medical school. I recall with clarity the first lecture given by Dr. Othmar Solnitsky, Professor of Anatomy. He spoke to us not about striving for achievement or wealth, but about what it takes to be the Good Doctor. He spoke of compassion and devotion, of empathy, and of dedication and service. As we made our way in the world, doctors of my generation were certain that we were part of new, exhilarating directions in medical care.

Medical students today cannot possibly imagine what is in store for them. If it's anything like the progress I have witnessed, it will be beyond their wildest expectations. But given the slow, inexorable and stunning transition that Medicine has made from profession to industry, I wonder, where has Dr. Good gone? I can't help but believe, with as far as medicine has come, and for as far as it will likely go, we have lost something on our way to achieving miracles.

###

ABOUT THE AUTHOR

Victor Keyloun was born in Brooklyn, New York in 1935. His parents were both immigrants from Aleppo, Syria, and his father became a prominent player in the New York garment industry. The youngest of six children, Dr. Keyloun chose not to follow his siblings into the family business, and instead attended the College of the Holy Cross and later Georgetown University Medical School. He served two years in the United States Navy before completing his post-doctoral training at St. Vincent's Hospital and starting private practice in Greenwich Village, New York. After twenty five years in practice, Dr. Keyloun switched careers, helming a highly successful consulting firm that specialized in creating computer-based sales training material and medical education for pharmaceutical companies around the world.

Dr. Keyloun is the co-author of *The Coronary Care Unit*, a detailed history of the opening of the first coronary unit of its kind in New York City. His memoir, *A House by the Park*, is an unflinching account of growing up in a large, loving family ravaged by bipolar disorder. In addition to his two other books, *Dr. Good Has Gone* and *Murder, Madness and St. Vincent's*, Dr. Keyloun has written and produced four plays and is currently working on his first screenplay.

He lives with his wife, Carol, in the suburbs of New York City.

Made in the USA
Charleston, SC
17 August 2013